Get set for the English SATS with CGP!

This amazing CGP book is packed with realistic SATS-style questions, all completely up-to-date for the tests in 2017 and beyond!

It covers all the key reading, grammar, punctuation and spelling topics — ideal for pupils working at or towards the Expected Standard.

We've even included Practice Tests at the start and end of the book, so you can easily measure how much progress they've made!

CGP — still the best! ☺

Our sole aim here at CGP is to produce the highest quality books — carefully written, immaculately presented and dangerously close to being funny.

Then we work our socks off to get them out to you — at the cheapest possible prices.

Contents

Section Four — Punctuation

Section Five — Vocabulary

Section Six — Spelling

Published by CGP

Editors:
Chloe Anderson, Izzy Bowen, Emma Crighton, Joanna Daniels, Cathy Lear, Jack Perry, Holly Robinson, Rebecca Tate

With thanks to Catherine Heygate and Alison Griffin for the proofreading.
With thanks to Jan Greenway for the copyright research.

Thumb illustration used throughout the book © iStock.com.

ISBN: 978 1 78294 678 6

Printed by Elanders Ltd, Newcastle upon Tyne.
Clipart from Corel®

Based on the classic CGP style created by Richard Parsons.

About This Book

This Book is Full of KS2 English Questions

At the end of Year 6, you'll be tested on all the reading, grammar, punctuation and spelling you've learnt during Key Stage 2.

This book has questions on the key topics you might be tested on.

This book covers the key Learning Objectives for Year 6 of the National Curriculum.

This book also has two Practice Tests.
The one at the front of the book is to test how much you already know.
The test at the back of the book is to see how much more you can do after using this book.

The answers to all of the questions are at the back of this book.

This Book Matches Our Standard Revision Book

The Standard Revision Book can help you if you get stuck.
It explains the most important things you need to know to do well on your test.
It's also got example questions to show you how to answer test questions.

There are Learning Objectives on All Topics

Learning objectives say what you should be able to do.
Use the tick circles to show how confident you feel.

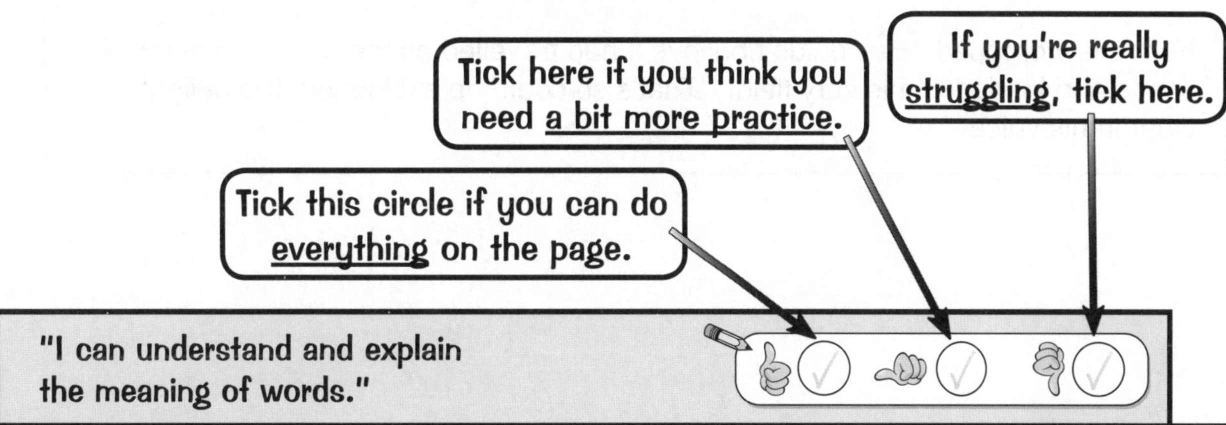

Practice Test 1

READING

Felix and his dad, Craig, go stargazing one night and make an interesting discovery.

"Dad, can you slow down a bit?" grumbled Felix.

"Just a little further to go. This meteor shower will be worth the effort. We should see lots of shooting stars!" Craig said, brimming with excitement.

He marched on ahead, carrying the telescope with ease, while Felix trudged along behind. Craig had a passion for stargazing and hoped that Felix would be inspired to take up the hobby too, but Felix wasn't as enthusiastic. It was a particularly brisk December evening and the wintry chill of the air was turning Felix's cheeks and nose red.

They finally made it to the top of the hill. Craig efficiently set up the telescope and began to adjust it, scanning the sky for Orion, his favourite constellation. Felix wished he was in his cosy room playing video games as Craig started reciting the same dull information about Orion that he always did when they were out stargazing. Felix had heard it so many times that he had memorised it.

"Felix, did you hear what I said?" Craig asked in frustration.

"Er, sorry?" Felix replied distractedly.

He was sitting hunched over on one of several sparse patches of grass, like islands surrounded by a swampy sea. The beam of his head torch was dancing on the ground as his head bobbed from side to side. He was absent-mindedly nudging a faded biscuit wrapper with his muddy shoes.

As Craig bent down to talk to Felix, he spied an unusual rock just centimetres from Felix's fingers. It was partly concealed, but Craig could see that it was dark grey in colour with rusty metallic flecks. His eyes widened in awe and he beamed.

"Felix, do you know what this is? It's a piece of meteorite!" Craig cried, "When a shooting star manages to land on the ground, it's called a meteorite." He held it aloft so his son could admire it in the moonlight.

Felix's jaw dropped. He couldn't believe it had travelled all the way from outer space and landed in this very field. "That's so cool!" he exclaimed, the delight clear in his voice.

1 *...while Felix trudged along behind.*
What does the word *trudged* suggest about the way Felix walked?

....

....

1 mark

2 In which season were Craig and Felix going stargazing?

....

1 mark

3 *Craig efficiently set up the telescope and began to adjust it...*
What does this show about Craig?

Tick **one** box.

He is inexperienced. ☐

He is clumsy. ☐

He knows what he's doing. ☐

He is very careful. ☐

1 mark

4 **Find** and **copy** a phrase which shows what Felix would rather be doing.

....

....

1 mark

5 Tick **two** items that Felix and Craig took with them.

compass ☐ mobile phone ☐

telescope ☐ head torch ☐

biscuits ☐

1 mark

6 **Find** and **copy** a phrase which suggests that the field was wet.

.... 1 mark

7 *It was partly concealed...*
What does the word *concealed* tell you about the rock?

Tick **one** box.

It was broken.	☐
It was hidden.	☐
It was dangerous.	☐
It was covered in dirt.	☐

1 mark

8 How can you tell that Craig was excited about finding the meteorite?

....

.... 1 mark

9 What does the word *aloft* tell you about how Craig held the meteorite?

.... 1 mark

10 Do you think Felix will become more interested in stargazing?
Explain your answer using information from the text.

....

....

.... 2 marks

Grammar, Punctuation and Spelling

11 Read the sentences below.
Tick the sentence that needs a **question mark** at the end.

Tick **one** box.

- You rang the bell, didn't you ☐
- Alex was looking for you earlier ☐
- I'll pass him the salt and pepper ☐
- Amber wants to know if you're leaving now ☐

1 mark

12 Draw lines to match each sentence with the correct **function**.
Each function box should only be used **once**.

Sentence	Function
Can I close the window	command
My sister is called Molly	exclamation
How horrible that was	question
Put away the ice cream	statement

1 mark

13 Add a **comma** into this sentence so that it is punctuated correctly.

I bought peas broccoli and a dozen eggs.

1 mark

14 Read the sentence below. Circle the two **conjunctions**.

Because Gail is going to cycle from London to York next month, she needs to do lots of training and buy a new bike.

1 mark

15 Read the sentence below. In the box, write the **contracted form** of the words that are underlined.

We <u>are not</u> allowed into the museum without a ticket.

☐

1 mark

16 Read the sentences below.
Tick the **preposition** that completes **both** sentences.

We're going to Majorca .... three weeks.

There were lots of multiplication questions .... the test.

Tick **one** box.

for ☐

during ☐

on ☐

in ☐

1 mark

17 Put a different **prefix** at the start of each word below to make a **new word**.

................arrange

................tidy

................heading

1 mark

18 Read the passage below. In each space, write the word in brackets with the correct spelling.

The storms had (**affected** / **effected**) our plans. All of the trains were delayed so we didn't know (**weather** / **whether**) we could get home.

1 mark

19 Read the sentence below.
What is '**the fancy new restaurant**' an example of?

After the ceremony, the Jones family went to the fancy new restaurant.

Tick **one** box.

a preposition ☐

a subordinate clause ☐

a noun phrase ☐

a main clause ☐

1 mark

Total

Word Meaning

This text describes a sunrise on a windy day.

The sun peeked over the horizon, its gentle rays bathing the fields in soft pink light. The rosy glow steadily grew in intensity as the sun inched its way higher. The birds had already been awake for hours, their tweeting and chirping echoing throughout the countryside. Rabbits, foxes and deer enjoyed their last hours of peace before they were disturbed by humans.

All of a sudden, a strong wind began swirling and howling and buffeting its way across the land, disturbing this peaceful scene. It turned the woods into emerald seas of leaves, the trees swaying to and fro like choppy waves in a storm. The gusts sped through the leaves, creating a soft roar that sounded like waves hissing over pebbles as they break on the shore.

1. *...the sun inched its way higher.*
   What does the word *inched* tell you about the speed the sun was moving across the sky?

   ....

   1 mark

2. **Find** and **copy** a word from the text that shows that the birds were singing.

   ....

   1 mark

3. *... swirling and howling and buffeting its way across the land...*
   What does the word *howling* tell you about the wind?

   Tick **one** answer.

   It was calm. ☐ It was quiet. ☐

   It was loud. ☐ It was scary. ☐

   1 mark

4. **Find** and **copy** a word from the text that shows that the leaves were green.

   ....

   1 mark

"I can understand and explain the meaning of words."

Retrieving Information

This text is about an unusual hobby called 'graffiti knitting'.

Graffiti Knitting

The art of knitting might make you think of older people, quiet evenings by the fire, or colourful but mismatched socks. But a new trend has made its way from the United States to Britain, and it couldn't be more different from that traditional view of knitting.

Graffiti knitting involves covering objects in public spaces with knitted material. The objects being decorated can be almost anything, from lampposts to bicycles to statues. One particularly keen graffiti knitter even managed to cover an entire bus in knitting — it took her a week, with some help from others. Graffiti knitting is sometimes done in secret because some people frown upon the fact that it's being done to public property. However, most of the time people don't mind the knitting as it doesn't damage or permanently change the objects involved.

So what is the point of all this needle-based fun? The idea is simply to brighten up public spaces and make them seem more friendly and welcoming. As a consequence, graffiti knitting often involves a vast selection of the most brightly coloured wool imaginable. Clashing colours are welcomed, and the more different patterns the better. As an alternative, it's also quite common to include faces when covering everyday objects, simply to give people passing by something to smile about. Catching a grin from a woollen telephone box as you walk down the street will certainly brighten up your day.

1 According to the text, what might knitting make people think of? Give **one** example.

....

1 mark

2 In which country did the graffiti knitting hobby begin?

....

1 mark

3 Give **two** things which can be covered in knitting according to the text.

1. ....

2. ....

1 mark

Retrieving Information

4 Why do some people disapprove of graffiti knitting?

....

1 mark

5 Give **one** benefit of graffiti knitting.

....

....

1 mark

6 Why do people knit faces on everyday objects?

Tick **one** answer.

To give people a fright.	☐	To make people smile.	☐
To improve public spaces.	☐	To promote telephone boxes.	☐

1 mark

7 Read each sentence and tick **one** box to show whether it is **true** or **false**.

	True	**False**
It is not always known who is behind the knitting.	☐	☐
Objects are sometimes damaged by graffiti knitting.	☐	☐
Graffiti knitting makes public spaces more friendly.	☐	☐
Colourful wool is often used by graffiti knitters.	☐	☐

1 mark

"I can retrieve and record information and identify key details from the text."

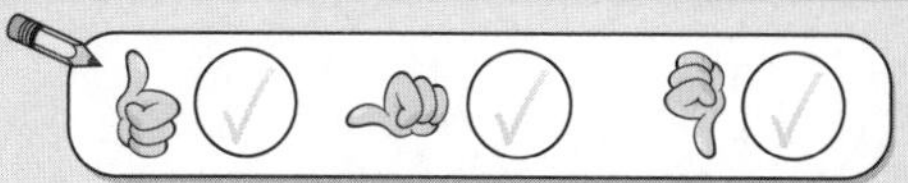

Summarising

This text is about a man who was rescued from a mountain in the Lake District.

Mountain rescue team warns of dangers after man falls on Helvellyn

The leader of a mountain rescue team has warned of the dangers facing walkers after saving a man on Sunday. "We'd like to remind everyone to please be safe on the mountains and always prepare well, especially in winter," she warned. "We see far too many people get into difficulty because they don't have enough experience or suitable equipment."

Over the weekend, an inexperienced walker in his forties plummeted 50m from Helvellyn, one of the highest peaks in the Lake District, after he slipped on a patch of ice in snowy weather because his shoes didn't have enough grip.

He attracted the attention of two nearby walkers after repeatedly calling for help. The walkers called the emergency services and gave him extra clothing, as he was poorly prepared for the conditions.

Using an air ambulance, the rescue team arrived quickly and soon realised that the man had broken his leg. He was rapidly transferred to hospital by helicopter to receive treatment.

"I'd like to thank the rescue team and the people who found me. I don't know how I would've got down the mountain without their help. I think I've learnt my lesson. In future I'll be much more careful to prepare better and take the correct equipment. I just didn't expect it to be so snowy."

His fall was certainly a good reminder that you should always prepare properly before going hiking, especially on mountains like those in the Lake District.

1 Read the second, third and fourth paragraphs of the text from *Over the weekend...* to *... to receive treatment.* What would be the best title for these paragraphs?

Tick **one** box.

- Man falls on Lake District mountain ☐
- Walkers need to prepare for bad weather ☐
- Man is rescued from Helvellyn ☐
- Walking in the Lake District ☐

☐ 1 mark

Summarising

2 Explain how the man was rescued.

....

....

....

2 marks

3 Which of the following best describes the man's behaviour?

Tick **one** answer.

friendly	☐	kind	☐
irresponsible	☐	scared	☐

1 mark

4 a) Tick the option which is the overall message of the text.

	Tick **one** box.
Walking is a dangerous activity.	☐
Hikers should always prepare properly.	☐
People shouldn't go hiking in the Lake District.	☐
Snowy conditions are always dangerous.	☐

1 mark

b) Explain how this is shown in the text.

....

....

....

....

2 marks

"I can summarise main ideas from more than one paragraph."

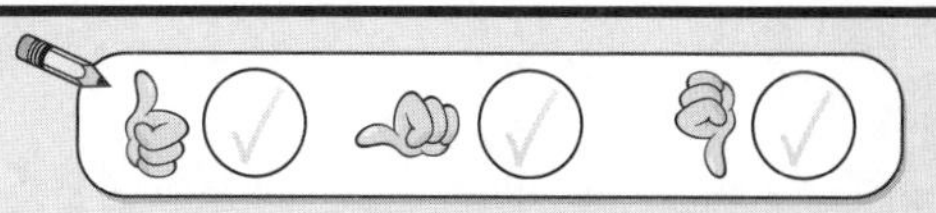

Making Inferences

This text is about someone trying surfing for the first time.

Annie was trembling with anticipation as she listened to the surfing instructor giving them safety instructions. She was finally having her first surfing lesson, and her excitement had turned into nervousness. It felt like her stomach was doing somersaults.

The instructor led the way as the group waded into the water. They had to paddle strongly against the waves, which loomed above their heads like watery mountains and rolled powerfully to the shore.

Annie turned her board towards the shore and got ready to catch her first wave. The instructor had told them they had to start paddling before the wave came so they were going fast enough to catch it. A large wave swelled up behind her and she began rapidly driving herself through the water.

She gasped as the water swooped underneath her, catching her board and carrying her with it. The board hummed as she sped towards the shore, effortlessly swept along by the wave. Annie grinned. She never wanted this experience to end.

The other members of the group congratulated her on how well she'd done, especially since this was her first lesson. Annie felt very pleased with herself.

1 *... she listened to the surfing instructor giving them safety instructions.* What does this suggest about surfing?

Tick **one** box.

- Surfing is easy. ☐
- Surfing can be dangerous. ☐
- Surfing is complicated. ☐
- Surfing is challenging. ☐

1 mark

2 How can you tell that Annie had been waiting a long time to try surfing?

....

1 mark

Making Inferences

3 *...the waves, which loomed above their heads like watery mountains...*
Explain how comparing the waves to mountains helps the reader understand what they looked like.

....

....

....

1 mark

4 How can you tell that Annie enjoyed surfing?

....

1 mark

5 Read each sentence and tick **one** box to show whether it is a **fact** or an **opinion.**

	Fact	Opinion
Surfing involves riding waves.	☐	☐
Surfing is a wonderful sport.	☐	☐
You have to start paddling before the wave comes.	☐	☐
Annie's surfing lesson was worth waiting for.	☐	☐

1 mark

6 Look at the paragraph that begins *She gasped as the water...*
How does this paragraph make the reader feel about surfing?
Use information from the text to support your answer.

....

....

....

....

2 marks

"I can make inferences and justify them with evidence from the text."

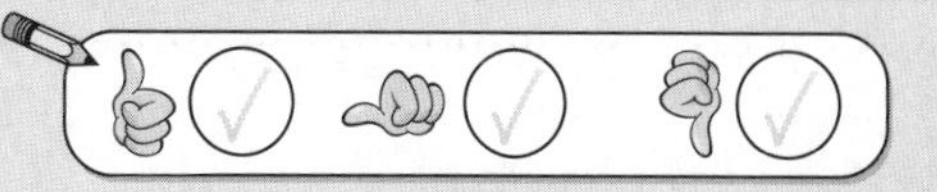

What Happens Next?

In this text, two children sneak off to the park at night.

The lengthy summer evenings were dragging on, and Matt and Simone were bored. In search of a thrill, they decided to sneak out to the park in the middle of the night. They crept out of their parents' house with ease, but then they faced an unexpected challenge — the towering park gates were locked.

"I can't climb those railings," Matt said hesitantly. "They look really high!"

"It'll be fine," Simone replied impatiently. "Come on!" And with that, she grasped the railings and hauled herself up to the top. Matt could see it had taken all her strength to do it, and he was certain he couldn't do the same.

"Simone, please get down," he said anxiously. "We should have arrived an hour ago when the gates were still open."

"But we wanted some excitement, and here it is!" said Simone crossly. "Why do you have to be so worried all the time?" She frowned as she perched effortlessly on top of the narrow iron rails. "So, are you coming or not?"

"Don't leave me alone!" wailed Matt, his knuckles white as he clung to the bars.

1. What do you think Matt would do differently if they decided to go to the park again? Use information from the text to support your answer.

....

....

....

2 marks

2. Do you think Simone will leave Matt and go into the park by herself? Use information from the text to support your answer.

....

....

....

2 marks

What Happens Next?

This text is about a new road being opened in a town.

Oakston Road opens this week

The mayor will officially open the newly completed Oakston Road on Friday. The new route circles around the town, meaning fewer cars driving through the centre.

Brian Hutchins, who has been campaigning for a new road for the past ten years, gave us his reaction: "Severe traffic jams have been a regular problem for us in the past," he said. "Fewer cars in Oakston means less pollution and less noise. I'm glad all the time and effort I've put in has been worth it. I'm not sure what to do with myself now though! My friends say I should have a rest, but I like to keep busy. And there are plenty of other good causes, aren't there?"

Not all residents are pleased with the construction of the road. Local business owners have complained that it will cause them to lose customers.

3. What do you think Brian Hutchins will do next? Use information from the text to support your answer.

....

....

....

2 marks

4. Based on the text, do you think the road will make things better or worse? Tick **one** box.

better ☐ worse ☐

Give reasons from the text to support your answer.

....

....

....

2 marks

"I can predict what will happen next based on information in the text."

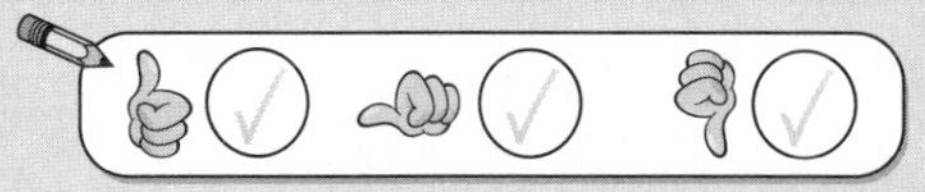

Structure

This text is an advert trying to persuade people to visit Japan.

Imagine clusters of cherry trees in full bloom, their soft pink petals forming heavenly clouds. Imagine these clouds against a perfect blue sky. Imagine a snowy mountain in the background, its clean whiteness contrasting perfectly with the blue and pink.

This is what you could see if you visited Japan in the spring. The island country is famed for its beautiful cherry blossom trees, whose delicate flowers attract hordes of admirers each year.

Japan has much more on offer in addition to cherry trees. Bustling cities like Tokyo and Yokohama attract thousands of visitors. A trip to the imposing Mount Fuji, whose almost perfectly triangular shape rises high above its surroundings, will live long in your memory. You can also gain a real sense of Japan's long history by visiting one of its striking castles.

With all this and more just waiting to be discovered, what's stopping you? Why not have the adventure of a lifetime? Experience Japan's cherry blossom season! Book your flights now from just £550 with Lion Air.

1. What is the purpose of the first paragraph?

....

....

1 mark

2. Why do you think the text starts with a long description of springtime in Japan before mentioning other aspects of the country?

....

....

....

1 mark

Structure

3 Look at the paragraph that begins *Japan has much more on offer...* What is the purpose of this paragraph?

Tick **one** box.

To give details about Mount Fuji. ☐ To describe castles. ☐

To show what else you can visit. ☐ To talk about history. ☐

1 mark

4 How does the last paragraph link back to the first paragraph?

....

....

1 mark

5 Draw lines from each box on the left to one on the right to match each part of the text with the correct quotation.

command	*Why not have the adventure of a lifetime?*
persuasion	*Imagine clusters of cherry trees...*
description	*... their soft pink petals forming heavenly clouds.*

1 mark

"I can explain how different parts of the text are related and describe the function of part of a text."

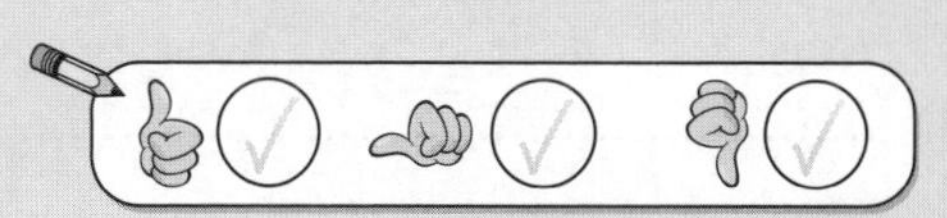

Choice of Language

This text is about paragliding, a sport where people hang from a 'wing' to fly.

Lucia was about to start her first solo paragliding flight. On her last flight with her instructor, she'd felt comfortable and relaxed, but now that the big day had come, her legs felt like jelly and she didn't even feel capable of lifting the wing that would keep her airborne.

After checking her kit and taking a few deep breaths, she was ready to go. Her instructor smiled at her. "You're all set," he said. "Soon you'll be in the air, soaring around like an eagle."

Lucia nodded. She bent her knees, paused and then leaped forwards. Her heart beat madly in her chest and her hands trembled like leaves in the wind. After a few seconds, she began to relax and realised how high up she was. She laughed to herself at the sheer joy of it. Gliding high above the ground was thrilling. She was delighted that she had been brave enough to do it alone.

1 *... her legs felt like jelly...*
What does this tell you about how Lucia feels?

....

.... 1 mark

2 *... soaring around like an eagle.*
What does this tell you about what the flight will be like?

Tick **one** box.

graceful ☐ unsteady ☐

short ☐ fast ☐

1 mark

3 Look at the paragraph that begins *Lucia nodded.*
Find and **copy three** words from this paragraph that show that Lucia is happy to be in the air.

1. ....

2. ....

3. .... 2 marks

Choice of Language

This is an extract from 'Rain in Summer' by Henry Wadsworth Longfellow.

How beautiful is the rain!
After the dust and heat,
In the broad and fiery street,
In the narrow lane,
How beautiful is the rain!

How it clatters along the roofs,
Like the tramp of hoofs
How it gushes and struggles out
From the throat of the overflowing spout!

Across the window-pane
It pours and pours;
And swift and wide,
With a muddy tide,
Like a river down the gutter roars
The rain, the welcome rain!

4 *Like the tramp of hoofs...*
What does this tell you about the rain?

Tick **one** box.

The rain is very light. ☐ It's raining a lot. ☐

The rain is quiet. ☐ The rain is loud. ☐

☐ 1 mark

5 Look at the last verse.
Find and **copy three** words or phrases from this verse that show that there is a lot of rain.

1. ....

2. ....

3. ....

☐ 2 marks

"I can identify how language can affect meaning."

Comparing

This text is about a boy who was very good at running.

Mark knew he was good at running. In fact, he knew he was *very* good at running. He was easily the best in his school. Today was the final of the county championships. Mark had been so confident leading up to the race that he hadn't bothered to do any training. He strutted around near the start line, telling the other boys they could fight it out for second place. All the other boys ignored him — they were used to his boasting.

But when the race began, he felt strange. His legs didn't seem as strong as usual and he was struggling to get enough breath. As hard as he tried, there were still boys ahead of him. He finished in fifth place, exhausted and miserable. All the other boys were hugging and congratulating each other, but they took no notice of Mark. Mark realised what a horrible person he had been.

"I'm sorry I was so arrogant," he said, nearing the others. "Will you forgive me?"

They hesitated for a second, and then decided. "Of course," said the boy who had won the race.

After that, Mark never boasted again. He won most of his races, but this was because he did at least two hours' training every day. He was friendlier towards his rivals, and even gave others tips to improve their running.

1. How does Mark's training at the start of the text compare to his training at the end?

....

....

1 mark

2. How is Mark different at the end of the text from the start? Explain your answer using examples from the text.

....

....

....

....

2 marks

Comparing

This text compares living in a city to living in the countryside.

Having access to lots of different places and events is often a reason people prefer living in a city. They may like being able to go to a nearby supermarket any time of the day or night, or being able to visit the theatre, cinema or museums. People also enjoy the crowds of a city and not having everyone know their name: people lead separate lives and can do whatever they like without everyone knowing about it. However, cities are often polluted and full of traffic. They can also be expensive to live in, especially popular cities such as London or Paris, where people can end up paying huge sums of money to live in tiny flats.

Most people think of the countryside as more peaceful than the city, as there are fewer cars and there's more to do outdoors. Many enjoy being able to spend time in the fresh air, perhaps doing sports or going for walks. However, for some people there is not enough happening in the countryside – they might have to travel miles to see a film or go shopping. Although houses in some beauty spots can be expensive, people are often able to buy bigger houses with gardens in the countryside, as there is more space available.

3 Compare the activities people do in the city and in the countryside. Use evidence from the text to support your answer.

....

....

....

....

2 marks

4 How do flats in cities compare to houses in the countryside?

....

....

1 mark

"I can make comparisons within texts."

Mixed Practice — Story

This text is about a girl who finds a mysterious letter hidden in a book.

Jas was a bookworm. She spent every second she could with her nose in a book. So when she came across an old book lying mysteriously on top of a wall near her house, nothing was going to stop her from picking it up. As she did, a letter fell out, labelled 'to the finder of this book'.

"I guess that's me!" Jas thought, tearing eagerly at the envelope.

Dear Finder,
I assume you're a book lover, as you've picked up this book. Go to the town library, section 090, shelf 090.56 and you'll find something you might enjoy.

Jas glanced at her phone. If she hurried, she'd just make it before closing time. She dashed to the library, but stopped short just inside the door; it was a vast old building, and she'd never been to the 090 section before. She was reluctant to ask a librarian though — how would she explain why she wanted that section? After some careful searching, she eventually found it. At first glance, the shelf seemed identical to the others in the section, but when she looked closer, she spotted a red leather book lying out of place on top of the others. Eagerly, she grasped it and flicked to the first page. It began:

There was a faraway world full of magic, ghosts and spirits — a mysterious world where witches flew in the air, ghosts haunted people and spirits lived in trees. But this mystical land could only be accessed by those who believed.

As she read, the book began to shimmer, and she felt herself being sucked towards the pages. The book was drawing her in, words flashing and pages flying before her eyes...

1 *She spent every second she could with her nose in a book.*
What does this tell you about how much Jas likes reading?

....

....

1 mark

2 Why did Jas pick up the book lying on the wall?

Tick **one** box.

Because someone had lost it.	☐	Because it was litter.	☐
Because she was a bookworm.	☐	Because it was old.	☐

1 mark

Mixed Practice — Story

3) **Find** and **copy** a word from the text that shows it was odd that there was a book on top of the wall.

....

1 mark

4) Read each sentence and tick **one** box to show whether it is **true** or **false**.

	True	False
Jas found a book inside her house.	☐	☐
Jas didn't know who wrote the letter.	☐	☐
Jas had lots of time to get to the library.	☐	☐
Jas asked a librarian where the 090 section was.	☐	☐

1 mark

5) Give **two** things that can be found in the world described by the red book.

1. ....

2. ....

1 mark

6) What do you think happens next in the story?
Explain your answer using information from the text.

....

....

....

....

2 marks

Mixed Practice — Poem

This poem, called 'The House With Nobody In It', is by Joyce Kilmer.

Whenever I walk to Suffern along the Erie track
I go by a poor old farm-house with its shingles broken and black;
I suppose I've passed it a hundred times, but I always stop for a minute
And look at the house, the tragic house, the house with nobody in it.

I've never seen a haunted house, but I hear there are such things;
That they hold the talk of spirits, their mirth and sorrowings.
I know that house isn't haunted and I wish it were, I do,
For it wouldn't be so lonely if it had a ghost or two.

This house on the road to Suffern needs a dozen panes of glass,
And somebody ought to weed the walk and take a scythe to the grass.
It needs new paint and shingles and vines should be trimmed and tied,
But what it needs most of all is some people living inside.

If I had a bit of money and all my debts were paid,
I'd put a gang of men to work with brush and saw and spade.
I'd buy that place and fix it up the way that it used to be,
And I'd find some people who wanted a home and give it to them free.

Now a new home standing empty with staring window and door
Looks idle perhaps and foolish, like a hat on its block in the store,
But there's nothing mournful about it, it cannot be sad and lone
For the lack of something within it that it has never known.

But a house that has done what a house should do, a house that has sheltered life,
That has put its loving wooden arms around a man and his wife,
A house that has echoed a baby's laugh and helped up his stumbling feet,
Is the saddest sight, when it's left alone, that ever your eyes could meet.

So whenever I go to Suffern along the Erie track
I never go by the empty house without stopping and looking back,
Yet it hurts me to look at the crumbling roof and the shutters fallen apart,
For I can't help thinking the poor old house is a house with a broken heart.

1. **Find** and **copy** a phrase from the first verse of the poem that suggests that the house is run down.

....

1 mark

Mixed Practice — Poem

2 *... And look at the house, the tragic house, the house with nobody in it.*
How does the word *tragic* make the reader feel about the house?

....

1 mark

3 Why does the narrator want the house to be haunted?

Tick **one** box.

So the house isn't alone. ☐ So someone lives there. ☐

To see a real haunted house. ☐ To talk to a ghost. ☐

1 mark

4 Look at the third and fourth verses of the poem, from
This house on the road... to *... give it to them free.*
Suggest **one** of the main ideas of these verses.

....

....

1 mark

5 Look at the fifth and sixth verses of the poem, from *Now a new home...*
to *... your eyes could meet.*
How does the description of empty new houses compare with that of empty old houses? Use evidence from the text to support your answer.

....

....

....

2 marks

6 *... the poor old house is a house with a broken heart.*
What does this make the house sound like?

....

1 mark

Mixed Practice — Non-Fiction

The subject of this text is a bird of prey called an osprey.

Ospreys: little-known birds

You may not have heard of ospreys — they are less famous than eagles, their more dramatic cousins, and far less common than buzzards, birds of prey which can regularly be spotted hovering in the air. But these yellow-eyed, powerful birds are well worth seeking out.

Unlike buzzards and golden eagles, ospreys feed exclusively on fish.
It is breathtaking to watch them dive suddenly and rapidly towards the water, sweeping their wings behind them and extending their claws forwards to catch their prey just below the surface.

The osprey was once far more common than it is today; many were killed in the 19th century, and they were nearly extinct in the UK by 1916. Happily, their numbers are now on the rise: they reappeared in Scotland in the 1950s, and the Lake District in 2001. In that same year, a conservation project reintroduced ospreys to Rutland Water in the East Midlands as well. There are now around 200-250 pairs of these remarkable birds in the country.

However, ospreys don't live in the UK all year round — in late summer, they migrate south to spend the winter in West Africa. They return in March to breed — this is why their UK population is given as a number of pairs, not a number of individuals.

Let's hope these wonderful birds continue flourishing in the UK.

1 What is the purpose of the first paragraph?

Tick **one** box.

To describe eagles.	☐	To compare birds of prey.	☐
To show that ospreys are interesting.	☐	To explain why ospreys aren't well known.	☐

☐ 1 mark

2 What is the population of ospreys like today compared to 1916?

....

☐ 1 mark

Mixed Practice — Non-Fiction

3. How can you tell that the author is pleased that the number of ospreys is increasing?

....

1 mark

4. Give the **two** places in the UK where ospreys began to live in 2001.

1. ....

2. ....

1 mark

5. Read each sentence and tick **one** box to show whether it is a **fact** or an **opinion.**

	Fact	Opinion
Ospreys are the most interesting bird of prey.	☐	☐
Some ospreys live in Scotland.	☐	☐
Ospreys come to the UK to breed.	☐	☐
Everyone should want ospreys to do well in the UK.	☐	☐

1 mark

6. Draw lines to match each word on the left to a word on the right which could replace it in the text.

exclusively	thriving
rapidly	stretching
extending	solely
flourishing	swiftly

2 marks

Nouns

1 Read the sentence below. Tick the word that is a **noun**.

We had a lot of fun yesterday.

Tick **one** box.

had ☐

a ☐

fun ☐

yesterday ☐

1 mark

2 Read the sentences below.
Underline the word '**brush**' where it is used as a **noun**.

You'll need a bigger brush to paint that wall.

Brush that dirt off your clothes before you come inside.

1 mark

3 Read the sentences below. Circle all the words that need **capital letters**.

On saturday, I am going on holiday to spain with my parents.

My friend frances and her family are coming too.

1 mark

4 Read the sentences below. Underline all the **nouns**.

The team won the competition. The fans were filled

with joy and admiration.

1 mark

"I can identify different types of noun."

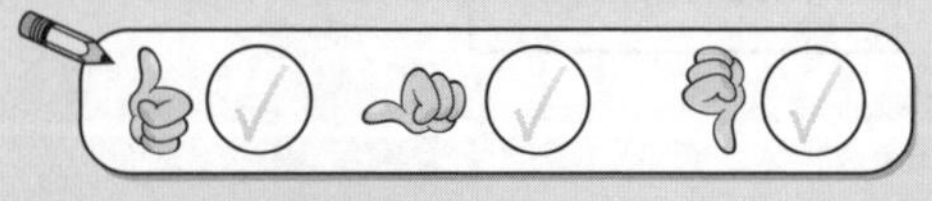

Verbs

1 Read the sentences below and circle all the **verbs**.

Tim walked forty miles and raised some money for charity.

1 mark

2 The sentence below contains one error.
Circle the error and write the correction in the box.

She ride her bike whenever she is bored.

1 mark

3 Read the sentence below. Put **V** in the box under the **verb**, **S** in the box under the **subject** and **O** in the box under the **object**.

Emma ran to the canal.

1 mark

4 Read the sentences below. Tick the two sentences that include a **modal verb**.

Tick **two** boxes.

Tilly is going to the hospital.

We should have a salad for lunch.

I might walk home this evening.

Samuel went to the rugby match.

1 mark

"I know what verbs are and how to use them."

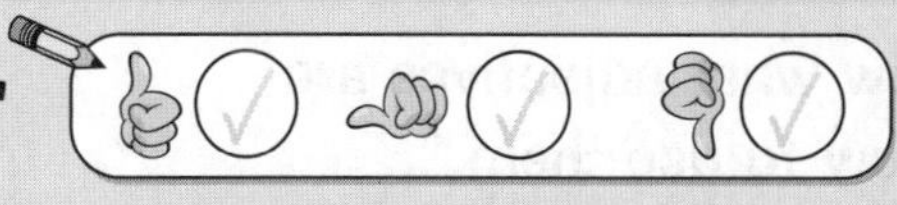

Adjectives

1 Read the sentences below and circle all the **adjectives**.

The hotel we stayed in was fantastic. It had enormous rooms and the beds were extremely comfortable.

1 mark

2 Complete the sentence below by filling in the gap with an appropriate **adjective**.

Jon wore his .... jumper to work yesterday.

1 mark

3 Read the passage below. Write an **adjective** derived from the noun in brackets in each space. One has already been done for you.

It was very ....**icy**........... [ice] on the roads today. Everyone at school was .... [misery] because of the cold weather, but I was .... [hope] that it would get warmer soon.

1 mark

4 Complete the sentences below by filling in each gap with an **adjective** formed from the verb in the box.

annoy ↓

I was very .... when I got lost in the city centre. I had to

help ↓

ask a .... man for directions to the restaurant.

1 mark

"I know what adjectives are and how to use them."

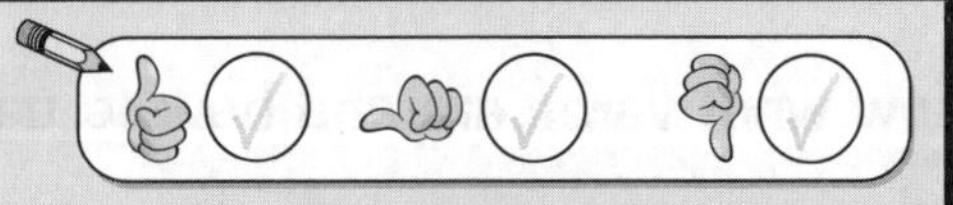

Adverbs

1. Read the sentence below. Tick the word that is an **adverb**.

We quickly ate the lovely birthday cake.

Tick **one** box.

quickly ☐

ate ☐

lovely ☐

birthday ☐

1 mark

2. Complete the sentence below by filling in the gap with an appropriate **adverb**.

Chris played .... with his friends for the rest of the day.

1 mark

3. Read the sentence below. Tick **one** box to show the position of the **adverb**.

I think we should get the bus tomorrow.

☐ ☐ ☐ ☐

1 mark

4. Read the sentences below and circle the two **adverbs**.

I am eagerly looking forward to going shopping. I will probably buy myself a new pair of shoes.

1 mark

5. Read the sentence below and circle the **adverbial**.

Despite the cold weather, Annabelle wore her favourite flip-flops.

1 mark

"I know what adverbs are and how to use them."

Prepositions

1 Read the sentence below. Put a tick by the word that is a **preposition**.

We went walking in the forest.

Tick **one** box.

We ☐
walking ☐
in ☐
the ☐

1 mark

2 Read the sentences below. Circle all the **prepositions**.

We played hide and seek after dinner. I hid under the stairs, Jill was behind the sofa, and Sarah shut herself inside the cupboard.

1 mark

3 Read the sentences below.
Tick the **preposition** that completes **both** sentences.

The taxi drove us .... the village.

We came in .... the front door.

Tick **one** box.

over ☐
into ☐
through ☐
on ☐

1 mark

"I know what prepositions are and how to use them."

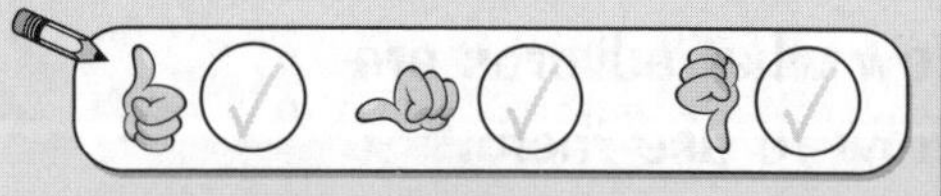

Pronouns

1 Read the sentence below.
Tick the pair of **pronouns** that best completes the sentence.

He said that .... were better at basketball than ....

Tick **one** box.

- he me ☐
- you me ☐
- you mine ☐
- they mine ☐

1 mark

2 Read the sentences below and underline the **possessive pronoun**.

She said that the skateboard in the shed is yours if you want it.

1 mark

3 Read the sentences below. Replace the words that are underlined with the correct **pronoun**.

When we got to the beach, <u>the beach</u> was very busy.

↓ ☐

My parents got stuck in traffic, so <u>my parents</u> were late for the show.

↓ ☐

I walked over to John and asked <u>John</u> if he knew what time it was.

↓ ☐

1 mark

"I know what pronouns are and how to use them."

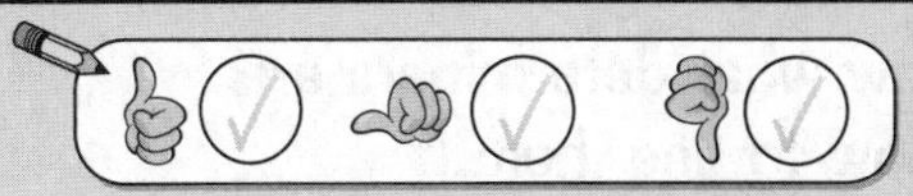

Determiners

1 Read the sentence below. Draw lines to match each sentence to its missing **determiner**. You should use each determiner **once**.

I wanted __________ cup of hot chocolate, but we had no milk.	a
They didn't have any left at __________ local shop either.	an
While I was there, I bought some juice and __________ apple.	the

1 mark

2 Read the sentence below. Put a tick by the word that is a **determiner**.

These pens are running out of ink.

Tick **one** box.

These ☐

are ☐

out ☐

of ☐

1 mark

3 Read the sentence below and circle the three **determiners**.

We ate the chicken and five potatoes for our dinner.

1 mark

4 Complete the sentence below by filling in the gap with an appropriate **determiner**.

They had .... spare rooms.

1 mark

"I know what determiners are and how to use them."

Mixed Practice

1 Read the sentence below.
Which **word class** does the word '**laughter**' belong to?

The room was filled with **laughter**.

Tick **one** box.

noun ☐

verb ☐

adjective ☐

preposition ☐

1 mark

2 Circle the **subject** and underline the **object** in the sentence below.

Layla really loved presents.

1 mark

3 Put a tick in each row of the table below to show whether the words in bold are **adjectives** or **adverbs**.

Sentence	Adjective	Adverb
She looked at him **seriously**.		
We made some **delicious** bread.		
Angie has a **friendly** rabbit.		
We're going to the zoo **today**.		

1 mark

4 Write down the correct **possessive pronoun** to replace the word or words that are underlined in each sentence.

The house belongs to <u>my grandmother</u>. The house is ....

The caravan is owned by <u>my friends</u>. The caravan is ....

The coat belongs to <u>me</u>. The coat is ....

1 mark

Mixed Practice

5 Complete the sentences below by filling in each gap with an **adjective** formed from the verb in the box.

interest

My parents are definitely .... in buying one of the puppies.

play

We went to visit them today, and they were very ....

1 mark

6 Read the sentence below and circle the two **adverbs**.

It was raining yesterday, so we reluctantly cancelled the match.

1 mark

7 Read the sentences below and circle the **modal verb** in each one.

She said she would leave her house at lunchtime.

You can have a pudding when you finish your vegetables.

I know there must be a mop around here somewhere.

1 mark

8 Put a letter in each box to show which **word class** the words belong to.

pronoun A	preposition B	determiner C	adjective D

After Sonia's party, we helped her tidy the house. It wasn't very enjoyable.

↑ ☐ (After) ↑ ☐ (her) ↑ ☐ (tidy) ↑ ☐ (enjoyable)

1 mark

Sentences

1 Read the sentence below. Tick **one** box to show the sentence's **function**.

The bus stop is at the end of the road

Tick **one** box.

a statement ☐

an exclamation ☐

a command ☐

a question ☐

1 mark

2 Write a **question** on the line below that begins with the word '**what**'.

What ....

1 mark

3 Look at the table below. Change the question into a **command**.
Write the command in the right-hand column.

Question	Command
Will you buy the rabbit?	

1 mark

4 Read the sentences below.
Tick the sentence which is an **exclamation**.

Tick **one** box.

Come over here ☐

I'm riding my bike ☐

Where are you going ☐

What a loud noise that was ☐

1 mark

"I can identify different types of sentences."

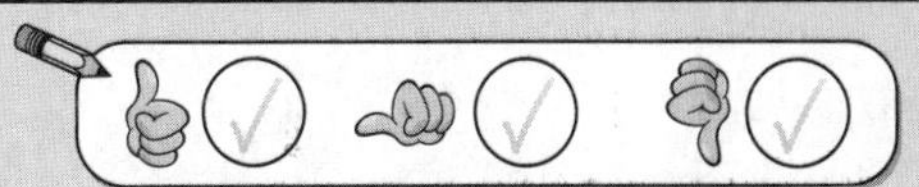

Clauses and Phrases

1 Read the sentences below. Underline the **main clause** in each sentence.

When he saw us, the otter swam away quickly.

You must do your chores, even though you don't want to.

I returned the jumper because it was too big.

Since it was Friday, Yasmin was allowed to stay up late.

1 mark

2 Look at the table below. Put a tick in each row to show whether the clause in **bold** is a **main** clause or a **subordinate** clause.

Sentence	Main clause	Subordinate clause
I took the dog for a walk before going to school.		
Although it was raining, we went to the beach.		
While we waited for the train, **we chatted about our trip**.		

1 mark

3 Read the sentence below.
What is '**until the train was empty**' an example of?

The passengers weren't allowed to get on until the train was empty.

Tick **one** box.

a subordinate clause ☐

a noun phrase ☐

an adverbial phrase ☐

a main clause ☐

1 mark

Clauses and Phrases

4 Read the sentence below.
Underline the longest **noun phrase** there is in the sentence.

The happy little bird flew around the garden.

1 mark

5 Read the sentences below.
Underline the **subordinate clause** in each sentence.

While I am on holiday, I go to bed later than usual.

I ate the whole cake although I soon felt sick.

Tristram joined a tennis club because he wanted to make new friends.

Since she had been caught, the robber confessed to her crime.

1 mark

6 Look at the table below. Add your own words before and after the noun to make your own **noun phrase**. One has already been done for you.

Noun	Noun phrase
the watch	the gold watch on my wrist
the dog	

1 mark

7 Rewrite the sentence below so it starts with the **adverbial**. Only use the words from the sentence, and make sure you use correct punctuation.

We're going to buy some sweets after school.

....

1 mark

"I can identify different clauses and phrases."

Conjunctions

1 Read the sentences below.
Choose a **conjunction** from the box to fill each gap and write it on the line.
You can only use each conjunction **once**.

and	but	while

Pari went to the school disco, ... Omar felt too unwell to go.

Yesterday, Joe went to the park .... to the shopping centre.

Juliette's dad cooked dinner .... her mum was at the dentist.

1 mark

2 Read the sentences below.
Circle all the **conjunctions**.

We should stay inside so we don't get wet. It will be sunny again soon and we will continue our walk, but the ground may still be wet.

1 mark

3 Put a tick in each row of the table below to show whether the conjunction in bold is a **co-ordinating conjunction** or **subordinating conjunction**.

Sentence	Co-ordinating conjunction	Subordinating conjunction
Joey plays the violin **and** Lily plays the trombone.		
The class enjoyed the book **because** it was funny.		
We could go bowling **or** to the cinema.		

1 mark

"I can link ideas together using conjunctions."

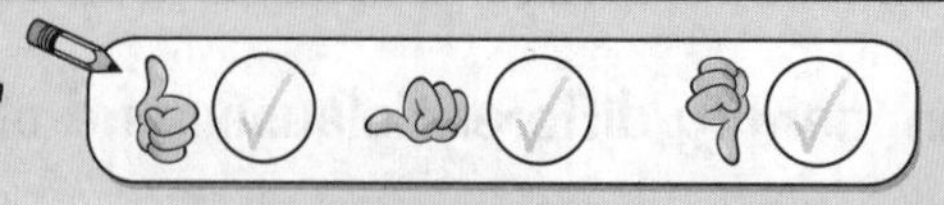

Active and Passive

1 Read the sentences below.
Tick the sentence which is written in the **active voice**.

Tick **one** box.

An assembly was called by the headmaster. ☐

He talked about helping others. ☐

A bake sale was organised by Year 6. ☐

The money raised was donated by the school. ☐

1 mark

2 Read the sentences below.
Tick a box in each row to show whether the sentence is written in the **passive voice** or the **active voice**.

Sentence	Passive	Active
The eggs were whisked by the chef.		
My bedroom is often very cold in the winter.		
The article was written by a famous scientist.		

1 mark

3 Rewrite the sentence below so that it is in the **passive voice**. Use the words from the sentence, and add extra words where appropriate.

Ellis watered the plant.

....

1 mark

"I can identify active and passive sentences."

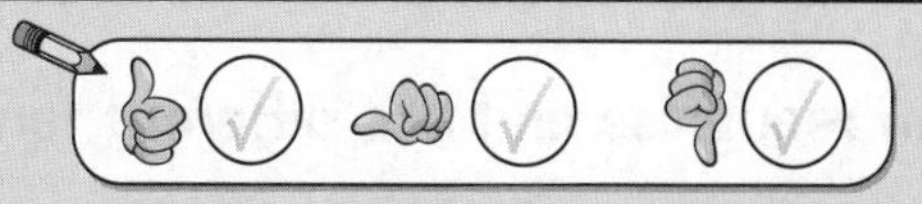

Tenses

1 Read the sentences below.
Tick the sentence which is written in the **present tense**.

Tick **one** box.

The dogs slept in the kitchen or outside the house. ☐

Georgia told Niall about her holiday in France. ☐

That coat in the window is not for sale. ☐

Before the concert, we had dinner with our friends. ☐

1 mark

2 Read the passage below. Change all the underlined verbs from the **present tense** to the **simple past tense**. One has been done for you.

At lunchtime, Jim, Lucy and I <u>play</u> football in the playground.

↓

played

Marco <u>asks</u> to play with us. He <u>joins</u> Lucy's team as the goalkeeper.

↓ ↓

☐ ☐

Lucy and Marco <u>win</u> the game, but we'll win next time.

↓

☐

1 mark

3 Read the passage below. Underline the verb form that is in the **present perfect**.

My hamster is called Butter. We got her two years ago.

She has lived in a cage in my bedroom ever since.

1 mark

"I can recognise and use different tenses."

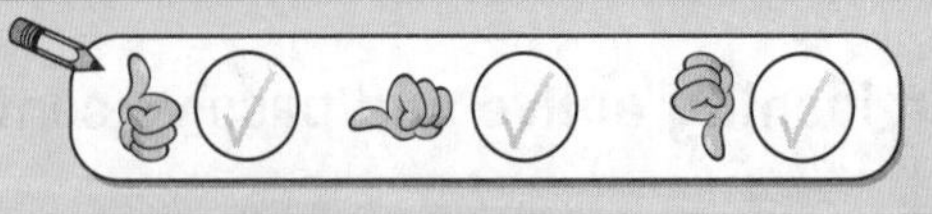

Formal and Informal Writing

1 Read the sentence below. Replace the underlined word with a **more formal** word. Write the word in the box.

Mrs Daniels asked me to watch the younger <u>kids</u>.

[ ]

1 mark

2 Read the sentences below. Tick the **two** sentences which are **formal**.

Tick **two** boxes.

- I look forward to receiving your reply shortly. ☐
- The view is beautiful, isn't it? ☐
- My family usually remains at home for Christmas. ☐
- Nicole wasn't keen to go to the play. ☐

1 mark

3 Look at the table below. Put a tick in each row to show whether each sentence is **formal** or **informal**.

Sentence	Formal	Informal
Crossing the road without looking is unwise.		
We'll go to the pool before breakfast, won't we?		
She wasn't on her way to the library.		

1 mark

4 Rewrite the sentence below so that it is **more formal**.

Jane isn't going to the party.

....

1 mark

"I can recognise formal and informal writing."

Standard and Non-Standard English

1 Read the sentences below. In each box, write a **Standard English form** of the word that is underlined.

Yesterday, we <u>was</u> helping my aunt paint her kitchen.

We <u>done</u> all of the work easily, so we haven't got <u>nothing</u> to do now.

1 mark

2 Read the sentences below. Complete the sentences using **Standard English** by circling one verb from each pair in brackets.

Claire and Lila (**goes / go**) to Australia on Saturday.

Peter (**saw / seen**) an excellent musical when he was in London.

Unfortunately, I haven't got (**none / any**) left.

1 mark

3 Read the sentences below.
Tick the sentence that's written in **Standard English**.

Tick **one** box.

My brothers hadn't seen nobody. ☐

Finish your lunch quickly so we can play outside. ☐

Cho threw the ball perfect into the net. ☐

Rowan said he hadn't done nothing wrong. ☐

1 mark

"I know the difference between Standard and non-Standard English."

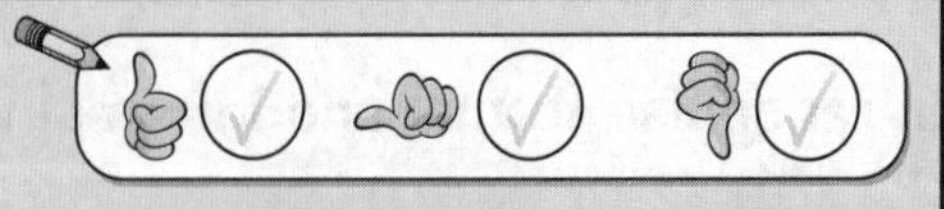

Mixed Practice

1 Read the sentences below.
Underline the **main clause** in each sentence.

Although we won the game, we thanked the other team.

Lisa showed me her story while Jan was busy in the kitchen.

My mum made me stay at home because I felt unwell.

1 mark

2 Draw lines to match each sentence with the correct **function**.
Each function box should only be used **once**.

Sentence	Function
Bring your work here	statement
Which cake did you want	question
My house is on the next road	exclamation
How wonderful the show was	command

1 mark

3 Read the sentences below.
Circle all the **conjunctions**.

If you're bored, try reading or drawing. You could also visit a friend and play a board game, although you might not win!

1 mark

4 Read the sentences below.
Tick the sentence that uses the **present perfect form**.

Tick **one** box.

Magicians must keep their methods secret. ☐

The Romans built a wall between Britain and Scotland. ☐

Angela was at the circus too — she was sitting behind us. ☐

Samira has watched every rugby match this season. ☐

1 mark

Mixed Practice

(5) Read the sentences below. Complete the sentences using **Standard English** by circling one verb from each pair in brackets.

I (**done / did**) my last project with Tahsin — it was about comets.

Those dogs outside are howling (**strange / strangely**).

1 mark

(6) Read the sentence below. Replace the underlined word with a **more formal** word. Write the word in the box.

I <u>reckon</u> that everyone should be treated equally.

1 mark

(7) Read the sentence below.
What is '**the silly clown with the red nose**' an example of?

Kingston laughed when he saw **the silly clown with the red nose**.

Tick **one** box.

an adverbial phrase ☐

a main clause ☐

a noun phrase ☐

a subordinate clause ☐

1 mark

(8) Read the sentence below.
Circle the two words that show the **tense** in the sentence.

Serena moved to Wales because her mum got a new job.

1 mark

(9) Rewrite the sentence below so that it is in the **passive voice**. Use the words from the sentence, and add extra words where appropriate.

My family built this house.

....

1 mark

Punctuating Sentences

1 Read the sentences below.
Circle all the words that need **capital letters**.

next weekend, i am going on a trip with my friend susan. we are catching the train to edinburgh on saturday morning.

☐ 1 mark

2 Read the sentences below.
Tick the sentence that needs a **question mark** at the end.

Tick **one** box.

Ask Sonam who she has invited to her party	☐
Who gets first prize will be decided by the judges	☐
I know who he is buying the gift for	☐
Who do you think will win the cricket match	☐

☐ 1 mark

3 Read the options below.
Tick the option that uses **full stops** correctly.

Tick **one** box.

Gordon often goes walking in the mountains. He likes to take lots of photographs of the scenery.	☐
Gordon often goes walking. In the mountains he likes to take lots of photographs. Of the scenery.	☐
Gordon often goes walking in the mountains he likes. To take lots of photographs of the scenery.	☐
Gordon often goes walking in the mountains he likes to take. Lots of photographs of the scenery.	☐

☐ 1 mark

4 The sentence below is missing an **exclamation mark**.
Tick **one** box to show where the exclamation mark should go.

"Look out☐" Geraldine shouted☐ as someone ran☐ in front of her trolley.☐

☐ 1 mark

"I can use capital letters, full stops, exclamation marks and question marks."

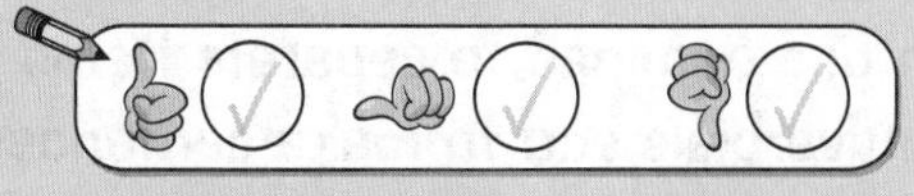

Commas

1 The sentence below is missing a **comma**.
Tick **one** box to show where the comma should go.

At the corner shop, I bought bread a litre of milk and the local newspaper.

☐ ☐ ☐ ☐

1 mark

2 Read the options below.
Tick the option that uses **commas** correctly.

Tick **one** box.

The farmer's dogs include, a collie a labrador a greyhound and a whippet. ☐

The farmer's dogs, include a collie, a labrador, a greyhound and a whippet. ☐

The farmer's dogs include a collie, a labrador, a greyhound and, a whippet. ☐

The farmer's dogs include a collie, a labrador, a greyhound and a whippet. ☐

1 mark

3 Read the sentence below.
Insert the missing **comma** so that the sentence is punctuated correctly.

After feeding the seagulls Bart got onto his bike and cycled home.

1 mark

4 Read the two sentences below. Explain how the meaning of the sentence is changed when the **commas** are added.

Non-fiction authors who spend more time studying write better books.

Non-fiction authors, who spend more time studying, write better books.

....

....

1 mark

"I can use commas to separate items in lists, after adverbials and to make sentences clearer."

Apostrophes

1 Read the sentences below.
Tick the sentence which uses an **apostrophe** correctly.

Tick **one** box.

All of the artists painting's were lost in the fire. ☐

All of the artists' paintings were lost in the fire. ☐

All of the artists paintings' were lost in the fire. ☐

All of the artists's paintings were lost in the fire. ☐

☐ 1 mark

2 Read the sentences below.
Circle the word that includes an **apostrophe** for **possession**.

I'll need to run if I'm going to catch the start of the film. Tiffany's brother has seen it and he's said the beginning is the best part.

☐ 1 mark

3 Write the **contracted forms** of the words on the left, using **apostrophes** in the correct places.

I have ....

she will ....

should not ....

they are ....

☐ 1 mark

4 Circle all the words in the sentences below that should have an **apostrophe**.

Sometimes, Walters cats go for a walk. Theyll often wander to Mrs Williamss house down the road.

☐ 1 mark

"I can use apostrophes to make contracted forms and to show possession."

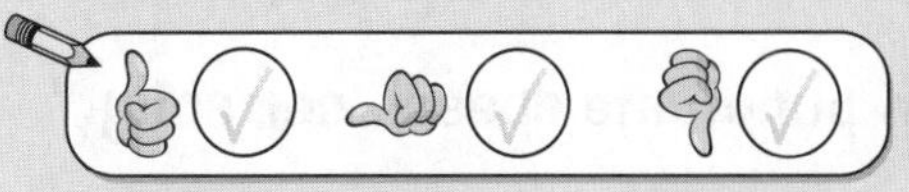

Inverted Commas

1 Read the sentences below.
Tick the sentence that uses **inverted commas** correctly.

Tick **one** box.

"It is going to be cloudy" today, said the weather reporter. ☐

It is going to be "cloudy today, said the weather" reporter. ☐

"It is going to be cloudy today," said the weather reporter. ☐

"It is going to be cloudy today, said the weather reporter. ☐

1 mark

2 Insert the missing **inverted commas** into the sentence below.

What's all that noise ? Ayaka asked , after waking suddenly .

1 mark

3 Read the sentence below. Your friend has asked you to help them to punctuate the sentence correctly. Which **two changes** would you suggest?

"I would like to join the basketball club" said Bill!

Tick **two** boxes.

Move the exclamation mark after the word 'join'. ☐

Replace the exclamation mark with a full stop. ☐

Put a comma after the word 'join'. ☐

Put a comma after the word 'said'. ☐

Put a comma after the word 'club'. ☐

1 mark

"I can punctuate speech correctly."

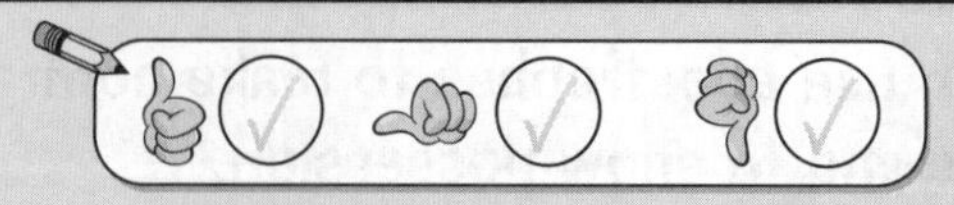

Colons, Semi-Colons and Dashes

1. Read the sentences below.
Tick the sentence which uses a **dash** correctly.

Tick **one** box.

Kath watched — the sun rise the sky was completely orange. ☐

Kath watched the sun — rise the sky was completely orange. ☐

Kath watched the sun rise — the sky was completely orange. ☐

Kath watched the sun rise the sky was — completely orange. ☐

1 mark

2. Read the sentences below.
Tick the sentence which uses a **colon** correctly.

Tick **one** box.

The bridge was shut: for the day there had been an accident. ☐

The bridge was: shut for the day there had been an accident. ☐

The bridge was shut for the day: there had been an accident. ☐

The bridge was shut for the day there had been: an accident. ☐

1 mark

3. Read the sentence below. Insert the missing **colon** so that the sentence is punctuated correctly.

The United Kingdom is made up of four nations Scotland, England, Northern Ireland and Wales.

1 mark

4. Read the sentence below. Insert the missing **semi-colon** so that the sentence is punctuated correctly.

Umair looked at his phone he found three new text messages.

1 mark

Colons, Semi-Colons and Dashes

5 The sentence below is missing a **dash**.
Tick **one** box to show where the dash should go.

Harold could tell it was Halloween all the shops were selling pumpkins.

↑ ☐ ↑ ☐ ↑ ☐ ↑ ☐

1 mark

6 Read the sentences below.
Tick the sentence which uses **semi-colons** correctly.

Tick **one** box.

Damon ordered a bowl of pasta; a (large) slice of garlic bread; and a glass of apple juice. ☐

Damon ordered a bowl of pasta a (large) slice of garlic bread; and a glass of apple juice. ☐

Damon ordered; a bowl of pasta, a (large) slice of garlic bread, and a glass of apple juice. ☐

Damon ordered a bowl of pasta, a (large) slice of garlic bread; and a glass of apple juice. ☐

1 mark

7 The sentence below is missing a **punctuation mark** in the place the arrow is pointing at. Which punctuation mark should be used?

I need to buy the following items a birthday card, a present and a stamp.
↑

Tick **one** box.

semi-colon ☐

dash ☐

colon ☐

full stop ☐

1 mark

"I can use colons, semi-colons and dashes correctly."

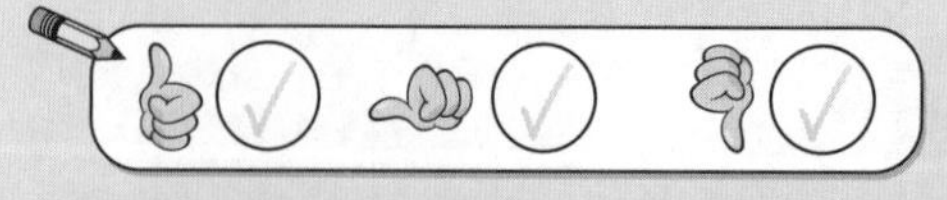

Adding Extra Information

1 Read the sentences below.
Tick the sentence that uses **dashes** correctly.

Tick **one** box.

Morgan — a qualified doctor checked — the man's pulse. ☐

Morgan a qualified doctor — checked the man's — pulse. ☐

Morgan — a qualified doctor — checked the man's pulse. ☐

Morgan a qualified doctor checked — the man's — pulse. ☐

☐ 1 mark

2 Read the sentence below. Insert **two commas** so that the sentence is punctuated correctly.

John asked Cindy his brother's best friend whether

she was planning to run a marathon that year.

☐ 1 mark

3 Read the sentence below.
Explain why a pair of **brackets** has been used in this sentence.

The hill above the town (a short walk from the post office)

gives a good view of the surrounding countryside.

....

....

☐ 1 mark

"I can use brackets, dashes and commas to add extra information."

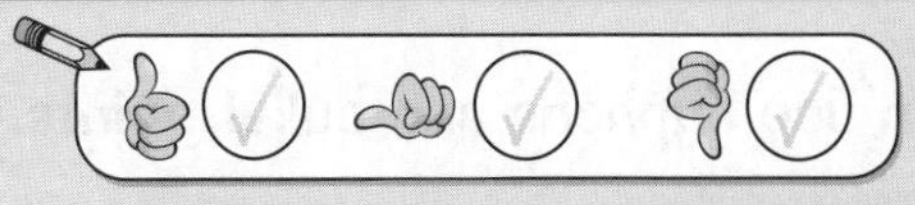

Hyphens and Bullet Points

1. Read the sentences below.
Tick the sentence which uses a **hyphen** correctly.

Tick **one** box.

Imran finished the race in a record-breaking time. ☐

Imran finished the race in a record breaking-time. ☐

Imran finished the race in a-record-breaking-time. ☐

Imran finished the race in a record-breaking-time. ☐

1 mark

2. Read the sentence below.
Write what Owen buys as a list of **bullet points** below.
Make sure you use correct punctuation.

At the gift shop, Owen buys a T-shirt, a cushion, two postcards and four coasters.

At the gift shop, Owen buys:

- ....
- ....
- ....
- ....

1 mark

3. Read the sentence below.
Insert the missing **hyphen** so that the sentence is punctuated correctly.

Samantha is friends with an actor and a well dressed businessman.

1 mark

"I can use hyphens and bullet points."

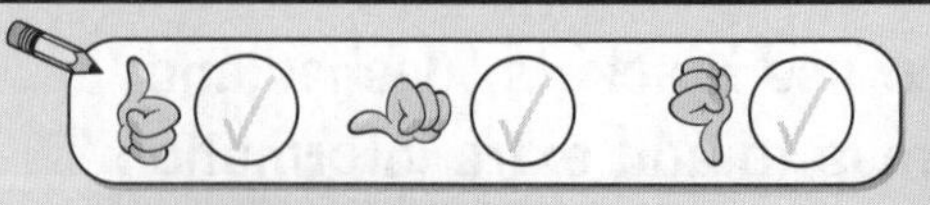

Mixed Practice

1. Read the sentences below.
Circle all the words that need **capital letters**.

next year, i am going on holiday to australia with my friend

sophie. we have booked to travel in april when it is cooler.

1 mark

2. The sentence below is missing **inverted commas**.
Tick **two** boxes to show where the inverted commas should go.

The bus conductor replied, Here's your change.

1 mark

3. Read the sentence below. Write the name of a **punctuation mark** that could be correctly used in the place of the **pair of dashes**.

Simi went to the seaside — her favourite place — to meet a friend.

....

1 mark

4. Read the sentence below. Insert the missing **semi-colon** so that the sentence is punctuated correctly.

The museum had many amazing things on display most of

them had come from a similar exhibition in Germany.

1 mark

5. Read the sentence below. Circle the word in the sentence that should have an **apostrophe**.

I enjoy reading childrens books. They usually

have exciting plots and interesting characters.

1 mark

Mixed Practice

6 Look at the table below. Put a tick in each row to show whether each sentence uses **commas** correctly or incorrectly.

Sentence	Correctly	Incorrectly
Felix, who was once a great piano player, had forgotten everything he had learned.		
At around, six o'clock Mera saw a bat fly past her window.		
Karin liked most vegetables, but she didn't like carrots, peas or spinach.		
After lunch, I went for a walk around the park.		

1 mark

7 The sentence below is missing a **hyphen**. Tick **one** box to show where the hyphen should go.

Phil's bad ☐ tempered ☐ puppy ☐ tore up the carpet ☐ this morning.

1 mark

8 Read the sentence below. Insert the missing piece of **punctuation** so that the sentence is punctuated correctly.

"I think it's time for us to leave" Noel whispered to Cheryl.

1 mark

9 Read the sentence below and write down the name of a punctuation mark that could replace '**but found that**'.

Tony peeked round the corner **but found that** there was nothing there.

....

1 mark

Mixed Practice

10 Read the sentence below.
Write Stanley's jobs as a list of **bullet points** below.
Make sure you use correct punctuation.

Stanley has a list of jobs for today: wash the car; take out the bins and the recycling; and clean the kitchen and the living room.

Stanley has a list of jobs for today:

- ....
- ....
- ....

1 mark

11 a) Add a **comma** in the sentence below so that it is clear that **only** Claire and Rafael went to the restaurant.

After they met Mr Fisher Claire and Rafael went to the restaurant.

b) Add **commas** in the sentence below so that it is clear that Mr Fisher, Claire and Rafael **all** went to the restaurant.

After they met Mr Fisher Claire and Rafael went to the restaurant.

1 mark

12 The sentence below is missing a **punctuation mark** in the place the arrow is pointing at. Which punctuation mark should be used?

Timothy had to take the bus to school ↑ it was too far to walk.

Tick **one** box.

comma	☐
exclamation mark	☐
question mark	☐
colon	☐

1 mark

Prefixes

1 Draw lines to match each word to the correct **prefix** to change its meaning.

Prefix	Word
anti	easy
un	use
auto	activate
de	clockwise
re	graph

1 mark

2 Put a different **prefix** at the start of each word below to make a **new word**.

.... belief

.... lead

.... market

.... visit

1 mark

3 Read the sentences below.
Write a **prefix** in each gap so the sentences make sense.

The yellow jacket was too big, so Martha decided to ....turn it.

Frances ....understood what the teacher said.

1 mark

"I know what prefixes are and how they change the meaning of a word."

Suffixes

1 Draw lines to match each word to the correct **suffix**.
You can only use each suffix **once**.

Word	Suffix
treat	ness
walk	ment
class	ify
personal	er
soft	ise

1 mark

2 Circle **two suffixes** which can be added to the word below to create new words.

kind

ly ate ful ify ness

1 mark

3 Look at the table below. Add a **suffix** to each adjective to make it a verb.

Adjective	Verb
multiple	
real	
simple	

1 mark

"I know what suffixes are and how they change the meaning of a word."

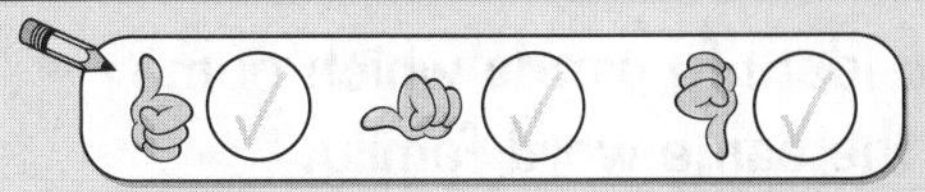

Word Families

1 Look at the word in bold below.
Circle the word which is in the same **word family**.

popular

police population position popcorn portable

1 mark

2 Look at the word family below.
What does the root '**sol**' mean in this word family?

solo isolation solitary

Tick **one** box.

sad ☐
far ☐
alone ☐
remote ☐

1 mark

3 Look at the word in bold below.
Circle all the words which are in the same **word family**.

stable

stairs stability unstable stamp adjustable

1 mark

4 Write down a word that belongs to the same **word family** as the words below.

forward foresee before

....

1 mark

"I can identify words which come from the same word family."

Synonyms and Antonyms

1 Tick **one** word which is a **synonym** of 'frequently'.

Tick **one** box.

surely ☐

regularly ☐

rarely ☐

surprisingly ☐

1 mark

2 Draw a line to match each word with its **antonym**.
You can only use each antonym **once**.

Word	**Antonym**
ancient	assist
obstruct	uninteresting
fascinating	unsuitable
appropriate	modern

1 mark

3 Read the sentence below.
Circle the two words that are **synonyms** of each other.

We were glad that their work was so precise — we needed accurate predictions before starting the new project.

1 mark

4 Give one word that is an **antonym** of 'superior'.

....

1 mark

"I know what synonyms and antonyms are and can come up with my own."

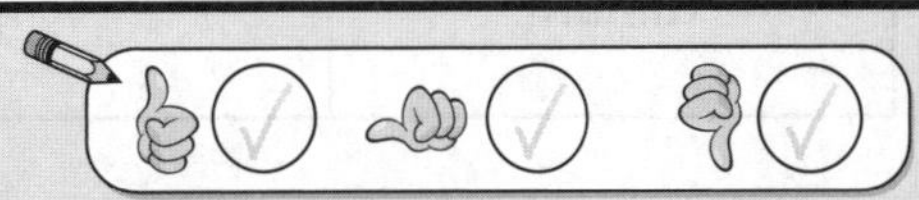

Mixed Practice

1 Read the sentences below.
Circle the two words that are **synonyms** of each other.

We all thought the restaurant was superb. I had a pie for my main course, and then an excellent apple crumble for dessert.

1 mark

2 Draw lines to match each word to the correct **prefix** to change its meaning. You can only use each prefix **once**.

Prefix	Word
dis	attach
re	hear
mis	appear

1 mark

3 Circle **two suffixes** which can be added to the word below to create new words.

equal

less   ful   ly   ify   ise

1 mark

4 Look at the table below. Complete the table by adding suitable **antonyms**.

Word	Antonym
delicious	
distant	

1 mark

Mixed Practice

5 Put a different **prefix** at the start of each word below to make a **new word**.

.... apply

.... cook

.... usual

1 mark

6 Look at the table below. Add a **suffix** to each verb to make it a noun.

Verb	Noun
run	
pay	

1 mark

7 Look at the word in bold below.
Circle all the words which are in the same **word family**.

art

chart start artistic apart artist

1 mark

8 Look at the word family below.
What does the root '**clar**' mean in this word family?

clarify declare clarity

Tick **one** box.

speak ☐
explain ☐
clear ☐
shout ☐

1 mark

Plurals

1 Look at the word in bold below.
Circle the **plural** of the word.

puppy

puppys puppies puppyes pupies puppis

1 mark

2 Put a tick in each row of the table below to show whether to add '**s**' or '**es**' to make each word **plural**.

Word	s	es
latch		
shirt		
potato		

1 mark

3 Look at the table below. For each word, write its **plural**.

Word	Plural
brush	
tooth	
turkey	
shelf	

1 mark

4 Read the passage below. Write the **plural** of the word in brackets in each space.

My sister invited some .... [person] over for lunch today.

We all had a salad with .... [tomato] and onion. I was

still hungry afterwards, so I had a few .... [cherry].

1 mark

"I can spell regular and irregular plurals."

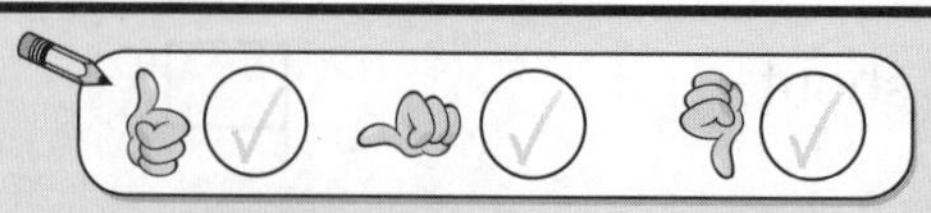

Prefixes and Suffixes

1 One of the words below is spelt **incorrectly**.
Circle the word and write the correct spelling in the box.

unable reform disimilar react inescapable

1 mark

2 Add the suffix '**ing**' to each of the words below.
Make sure each word is spelt correctly.

begin.......................

sit.......................

laugh.......................

garden.......................

1 mark

3 Look at the table below. Rewrite each word with the correct **spelling**.

Word	Correct Spelling
awtomobile	
subbmarine	
innteract	
suparstar	

1 mark

Prefixes and Suffixes

4 Look at the words below and tick the word that is spelt **correctly**.

Tick **one** box.

offitial ☐

essencial ☐

special ☐

crutial ☐

1 mark

5 Write each of these words with the **correct spelling**.

meaness ....

disolve ....

fameous ....

limitted ....

1 mark

6 Look at the table below. In each row, write the word made by combining the word and the **suffix**.

Word	Suffix	New Word
friendly	ness	
simple	er	
continue	ous	

1 mark

"I can spell words that have prefixes and suffixes."

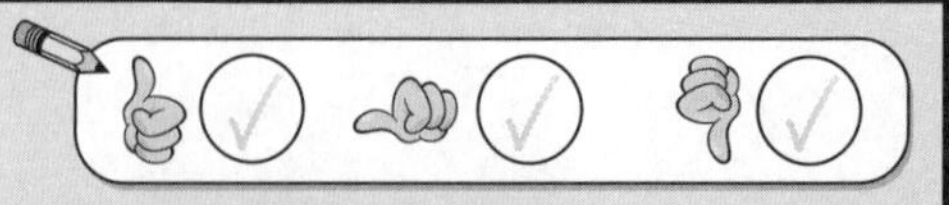

Homophones

1 Read the sentences below. Circle the correct word in brackets to complete each sentence.

We went to the cinema because we were (**board** / **bored**).

I asked my friends where they wanted to (**meet** / **meat**) for lunch.

Ellie took a (**piece** / **peace**) of paper and began to draw on it.

1 mark

2 Draw lines to match each word to its meaning.

Meaning	Word
an award	medal
above average	grate
to interfere	meddle
to shred into pieces	great

1 mark

3 Look at the words below. For each word, write another word that sounds the same but has a **different spelling**.

scene ....

aloud ....

mane ....

steel ....

1 mark

"I can spell different homophones."

Silent Letters

1 Look at the words below. Tick the word that is spelt **correctly**.

Tick **one** box.

narled ☐

knarled ☐

gnarled ☐

nharled ☐

1 mark

2 Complete the sentences below by adding the missing **silent letters** to the words in bold.

Jeremy ....**new** the way to the bus station.

We felt very **dou**........**tful** about the weather forecast that weekend.

I checked the time by looking at the watch on my ....**rist**.

1 mark

3 One of the words below is spelt **incorrectly**. Circle the word and write the correct spelling in the box.

carm white honour written numb

☐

1 mark

4 Read the passage below. In each space, write the word in brackets with the correct spelling.

We saw the .... [desine] for the new building as soon

as we .... [warked] into her office. We asked her about

it, but she wouldn't .... [anser] our questions.

1 mark

"I can spell words with silent letters."

Spelling Tricky Words

1 Look at the words below and tick the word that is spelt **correctly**.

Tick **one** box.

feild ☐

ceiling ☐

peirce ☐

sheild ☐

☐ 1 mark

2 Read the sentences below. Circle the correct word in brackets to complete each sentence.

I had three (**peices** / **pieces**) of pizza.

My best friend and I are in the same (**sceince** / **science**) class.

They decided that (**neither** / **niether**) of the hotels was good enough.

☐ 1 mark

3 Write each of these words with the **correct spelling**.

acept ....

suporter ....

mesage ....

succes ....

☐ 1 mark

Spelling Tricky Words

4 The sentence below contains one spelling mistake. Circle the word that is spelt incorrectly and write the correct spelling in the box.

We went to a factory and saw a mashine that makes chocolate.

[ ]

1 mark

5 Complete the sentences below by filling in each gap with a word that sounds the same as the word in the box.

threw

We always went into the house .... the side door.

fort

The cats often .... playfully with each other.

ort

We .... to go and see how Curtis is feeling.

1 mark

6 The words below are spelled incorrectly. Write each word with the **correct spelling**.

enuff ....

imposible ....

acess ....

skool ....

aparrent ....

1 mark

"I can spell tricky words."

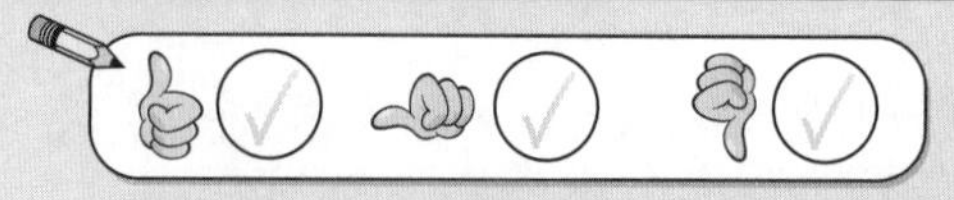

Mixed Practice

1 Look at the words below and tick the word that is spelled **correctly**.

Tick **one** box.

gnee ☐

nee ☐

knee ☐

nhee ☐

1 mark

2 Read the sentences below. Circle the correct word in brackets to complete each sentence.

Dilma had (**heard** / **herd**) the news on the radio.

I wasn't sure what to (**where** / **wear**) for the party.

The teacher started to (**right** / **write**) the instructions on the board.

1 mark

3 Read the passage below. Write the **plural** of the word in brackets in each space.

The .... [thief] tried to get into the house by climbing up

the .... [branch]. The police managed to catch them

because two .... [woman] spotted them.

1 mark

Mixed Practice

4 One of the words below is spelt **incorrectly**.
Circle the word and write the correct spelling in the box.

happiness initial understanding nerveous regretful

1 mark

5 Complete the sentences below by adding the missing **prefixes** or **suffixes** to the words in bold.

I need to buy my friend's birthday present but I keep **forget**................

I didn't need to wash the car — it was ....**necessary** after the rain.

On Saturdays we go **swim**................ in the pool at the local leisure centre.

1 mark

6 The words below are spelled incorrectly.
Write each word with the **correct spelling**.

parashute ....

bougt ....

unles ....

parcial ....

1 mark

7 Read the sentences below. Add the missing letters.

Mandy **rec**........**ved** a postcard from Josh.

Claudia couldn't **bel**........**ve** what she was hearing.

1 mark

Practice Test 2

Reading

The Giant's Causeway is a popular tourist attraction in Northern Ireland.

Marvelled at by hundreds of thousands of tourists each year, the Giant's Causeway is Northern Ireland's sole UNESCO World Heritage Site, situated on its northern coast. Around 40,000 rocks with almost flawless hexagonal shapes hug the coastline in a honeycomb-like formation. Volcanic activity millions of years ago caused this unique natural phenomenon — or did it?

Legend has it that thousands of years ago an Irish giant named Finn McCool constructed the causeway so he could make his way to Scotland to battle with his rival, Benandonner. When he saw up close how intimidating and huge the other giant was, Finn McCool fled back along the causeway with Benandonner in pursuit. Thinking quickly, Finn's wife dressed him up like a baby to avoid Finn being injured and to confuse Benandonner. Seeing such a large baby made Benandonner think about how frightening its father would be, and so he retreated.

There are several interesting rock formations at the Giant's Causeway that are clues to the legend. The Giant's Boot was supposedly left behind by Finn McCool as he fled from Benandonner. Another to look out for is the Camel. Finn's stone companion rests at the water's edge, another product of the volcanic activity in the area. Said to have travelled with Finn on journeys, the Camel now lives a lonely existence by the Causeway. Another fascinating sight to behold is the Wishing Chair. The structure is nestled among the rocks, providing a pleasant spot to have a rest or even a picnic.

Those who are curious about the legend of Finn McCool or the scientific explanation of how the Giant's Causeway was formed can learn more at the outstanding visitor centre nearby. Here, visitors can immerse themselves in the history of the area and admire the stunning scenery.

1 How many UNESCO World Heritage sites are there in Northern Ireland?

....

1 mark

2 *Around 40,000 rocks with almost flawless hexagonal shapes hug the coastline...*
What does the word *hug* suggest about the location of the rocks?

....

....

1 mark

3 *When he saw up close how intimidating and huge the other giant was...*
What does the word *intimidating* mean in the sentence above?

Tick **one** box.

dangerous ☐
frightening ☐
jealous ☐
strong ☐

1 mark

4 Why did Benandonner run away when he saw the 'baby'?

....

....

1 mark

5 What might have happened if Finn hadn't dressed like a baby?

....

1 mark

6 Name **two** sights that are said to be associated with Finn McCool.

1) ....

2) ....

1 mark

7 Tick the option which is the most suitable summary of the last two paragraphs of the text.

Tick **one** box.

Rock formations at the Giant's Causeway ☐

The rivalry between Finn and Benandonner ☐

Things to see when you visit the Giant's Causeway ☐

The visitor centre at the Giant's Causeway ☐

1 mark

8 *Visitors can immerse themselves in the history of the area...*
Which of the following is closest in meaning to the word *immerse*?

Tick **one** box.

escape ☐

learn ☐

relive ☐

surround ☐

1 mark

9 Compare the scientific explanation of the formation of the Giant's Causeway and the legend of Finn McCool. Use evidence from the text to support your answer.

....

....

....

2 marks

10 Which of these sentences describes a main idea of this text?

Tick **one** box.

Legends say that a giant built the Giant's Causeway. ☐

Finn McCool was a giant. ☐

The visitor centre is excellent. ☐

You can have picnics at the Giant's Causeway. ☐

1 mark

Grammar, Punctuation and Spelling

11 Read the options below. Tick the option which is punctuated correctly.

Tick **one** box.

Amani paints a lot she likes, to draw too. ☐

Amani paints. A lot she likes to draw too. ☐

Amani paints a lot. She likes to draw too. ☐

Amani paints a lot, she likes to draw too. ☐

1 mark

12 Read the sentences below. Put a tick in each row of the table to show whether the word is a **verb** or an **adjective**.

Johan visited the interesting monument on top of the hill.

He was disappointed because the wind blew his hat away.

Word	Verb	Adjective
visited		
interesting		
disappointed		
blew		

1 mark

13 Read the sentences below.
Circle all of the words that should start with **capital letters**.

my friend, agnes, lives in birmingham. i went to see her last thursday.

1 mark

14 One of the words below is spelt **incorrectly**.
Circle the word and write the correct spelling in the box.

deceive height efficient releif spicier

1 mark

15 Write a **question** on the line below that begins with the word '**which**'.

Which ....

1 mark

16 Read the sentences below. Underline the **main clause** in each sentence.

Ahmed's favourite subject is history, although he likes geography too.

Even though it was nearby, Amanda drove to the shop.

☐ 1 mark

17 The sentence below is missing **punctuation marks** in the places the arrows are pointing at. Which punctuation marks should be used?

Elmer can't eat eggs ↑ he is allergic to them ↑ but could have beans on toast.

Tick **one** box.

- inverted commas ☐
- brackets ☐
- hyphens ☐
- exclamation marks ☐

☐ 1 mark

18 Read the sentence below. Tick the sentence which is an **exclamation**.

Tick **one** box.

- Do you have a cat ☐
- What a nice bird that is ☐
- Milo has eight hamsters ☐
- Look at that dog ☐

☐ 1 mark

19 Read the sentences below.
Circle the two words that are **synonyms** of each other.

Grace's brother annoyed her because he borrowed her games console and broke it. It irritated her that he was so careless with her things.

☐ 1 mark

Total ☐

Answers

Pages 2-6 — Practice Test 1

Q1 *1 mark for a sensible answer, e.g.* He was walking slowly and dragging his feet.

Q2 winter *(1 mark)*

Q3 He knows what he's doing. *(1 mark)*

Q4 Felix wished he was in his cosy room playing video games. *(1 mark)*

Q5 telescope, head torch *(1 mark)*

Q6 a swampy sea *(1 mark)*

Q7 It was hidden. *(1 mark)*

Q8 *1 mark for a sensible answer, e.g.* Because his eyes 'widened in awe' and he was smiling.

Q9 *1 mark for a sensible answer, e.g.* He held it up high.

Q10 *1 mark for a simple answer, e.g.* Yes, because he was really excited when they found the meteorite.
2 marks for a more detailed answer, e.g. Yes, because he was so pleased when Craig told him they'd found a meteorite and he was amazed by the meteorite's journey.

Q11 You rang the bell, didn't you *(1 mark)*

Q12 Can I close the window — question
My sister is called Molly — statement
How horrible that was — exclamation
Put away the ice cream — command *(1 mark)*

Q13 I bought peas, broccoli and a dozen eggs. *(1 mark)*

Q14 Because, and *(1 mark)*

Q15 aren't *(1 mark)*

Q16 in *(1 mark)*

Q17 **re**arrange
untidy
subheading *(1 mark)*

Q18 The storms had **affected** our plans. All of the trains were delayed so we didn't know **whether** we could get home. *(1 mark)*

Q19 a noun phrase *(1 mark)*

Pages 7-27 — Reading

Word Meaning

Q1 *1 mark for a sensible answer, e.g.* The sun is moving very slowly.

Q2 tweeting / chirping *(1 mark)*

Q3 It was loud. *(1 mark)*

Q4 emerald *(1 mark)*

Retrieving Information

Q1 *1 mark for a sensible answer, e.g.* Quiet evenings by the fire.

Q2 the United States *(1 mark)*

Q3 lampposts / bicycles / statues / buses / telephone boxes *(1 mark for any 2 answers)*

Q4 Because it's being done to public property. *(1 mark)*

Q5 *1 mark for a sensible answer, e.g.* It makes public spaces look brighter.

Q6 To make people smile. *(1 mark)*

Q7 true, false, true, true *(1 mark)*

Summarising

Q1 Man is rescued from Helvellyn *(1 mark)*

Q2 *1 mark for a simple answer, e.g.* A helicopter took him to hospital.
2 marks for a more detailed answer, e.g. Other walkers called for an ambulance. The air ambulance rescue team then took him to hospital in a helicopter.

Q3 irresponsible *(1 mark)*

Q4a Hikers should always prepare properly. *(1 mark)*

Q4b *1 mark for a simple answer, e.g.* The text is about a man who had to be rescued because he wasn't properly prepared.
2 marks for a more detailed answer based on the text, e.g. The text starts and ends with the message that walkers need to be prepared. The middle section is about a man who didn't prepare properly and fell.

Making Inferences

Q1 Surfing can be dangerous. *(1 mark)*

Q2 She was 'finally' going surfing. *(1 mark)*

Q3 *1 mark for a sensible answer, e.g.* Mountains are tall, so this suggests that the waves are also very large.

Q4 She never wanted the experience to end / She grinned while she was surfing. *(1 mark for one point)*

Q5 fact, opinion, fact, opinion *(1 mark)*

Q6 *1 mark for a simple answer, e.g.* It makes the reader feel excited about surfing.
2 marks for a more detailed answer, e.g. Words like 'swooped' and 'sped' make the reader feel excited about surfing. She is swept along 'effortlessly' which makes the reader feel interested in trying surfing.

What Happens Next?

Q1 *1 mark for a sensible prediction based on the text, e.g.* He would have gone earlier.

Answers

2 marks for a sensible prediction with evidence from the text, e.g. Matt would have gone to the park earlier because he says 'we should have arrived an hour ago'.

Q2 *1 mark for a sensible prediction based on the text, e.g.* Yes, because she's already started climbing the gate.
2 marks for a sensible prediction with evidence from the text, e.g. Yes, because she asks Matt 'are you coming or not?' which suggests she'll go without him.

Q3 *1 mark for a sensible prediction based on the text, e.g.* He will find another cause to support.
2 marks for a sensible prediction with evidence from the text, e.g. He says 'I like to keep busy' so he will probably find other 'good causes' to campaign for.

Q4 *1 mark for a sensible prediction based on the text, e.g.* Worse, because the road means customers won't pass by local businesses.
2 marks for a sensible prediction with evidence from the text, e.g. Better, as there won't be as much traffic in the town centre. It will also reduce pollution and noise because there will be 'fewer cars' in Oakston.

Structure

Q1 *1 mark for a sensible answer, e.g.* To get the reader interested by creating a beautiful image in their mind.

Q2 *1 mark for a sensible answer, e.g.* Because the advert is trying to persuade people to go to Japan in spring.

Q3 To show what else you can visit. *(1 mark)*

Q4 *1 mark for a sensible answer, e.g.* It mentions Japan's cherry blossom season which is described in the first paragraph.

Q5 Command — Imagine clusters of cherry trees...
Persuasion — Why not have the adventure of a lifetime?
Description — ...their soft pink petals forming heavenly clouds.
(1 mark)

Choice of Language

Q1 *1 mark for a sensible answer, e.g.* She feels very nervous.

Q2 graceful *(1 mark)*

Q3 laughed / joy / thrilling / delighted *(1 mark for any 2 correct words, 2 marks for any 3 correct words)*

Q4 The rain is loud. *(1 mark)*

Q5 pours / swift / wide / Like a river / roars
(1 mark for any 2 correct words or phrases, 2 marks for any 3 correct words or phrases)

Comparing

Q1 *1 mark for a sensible answer, e.g.* He didn't train in the beginning, but by the end he trained every day.

Q2 *1 mark for a simple answer, e.g.* At the start, he is rude, but by the end he is friendlier.
2 marks for a more developed answer which makes reference to the text, e.g. At the beginning, Mark boasted and 'strutted around' because he's arrogant. At the end, he's more humble. He trains 'every day' and is 'friendlier'.

Q3 *1 mark for a simple answer, e.g.* People can go to shows in the city and do outdoor activities in the countryside.
2 marks for a more detailed answer based on the text, e.g. There are many things to do indoors in the city, like 'the theatre, cinema or museums'. The countryside has more outdoor activities, like 'doing sports or going for walks'.

Q4 *1 mark for a sensible answer, e.g.* City flats are often small but expensive. Houses in the countryside tend to be larger.

Mixed Practice — Story

Q1 *1 mark for a sensible answer, e.g.* She reads all the time, which tells you she loves reading.

Q2 Because she was a bookworm. *(1 mark)*

Q3 mysteriously *(1 mark)*

Q4 false, true, false, false *(1 mark)*

Q5 magic / ghosts / spirits / witches *(1 mark for any 2 correct words)*

Q6 *1 mark for a sensible prediction based on the text, e.g.* She will get sucked into the book.
2 marks for a sensible prediction with evidence from the text, e.g. Jas feels like she's being 'sucked' towards the pages so I think she will be pulled into the book and into the magical world she read about.

Mixed Practice — Poem

Q1 broken and black *(1 mark)*

Q2 *1 mark for a sensible answer, e.g.* It makes the reader feel sorry for the house.

Answers

Q3 So the house isn't alone. *(1 mark)*

Q4 *1 mark for a suitable main idea, e.g.* The poet wants to repair the house.

Q5 *1 mark for a simple answer, e.g.* Empty new houses aren't lonely, but empty old houses are.
2 marks for a more developed answer, e.g. Empty new houses aren't lonely because they've never been lived in. Empty old houses get lonely because they're used to people living in them.

Q6 *1 mark for a sensible answer, e.g.* It makes the house sound like a person.

Mixed Practice — Non-Fiction

Q1 To explain why ospreys aren't well known. *(1 mark)*

Q2 *1 mark for a sensible answer, e.g.* It is larger today.

Q3 *1 mark for a sensible answer, e.g.* The author says 'Happily' when writing about their rising numbers.

Q4 The Lake District / Rutland Water in the East Midlands *(1 mark)*

Q5 opinion, fact, fact, opinion *(1 mark)*

Q6 exclusively — solely
rapidly — swiftly
extending — stretching
flourishing — thriving
(1 mark for 2 or 3 correct answers, 2 marks for all 4 correct)

Pages 28-36 — Word Types

Nouns

Q1 fun *(1 mark)*

Q2 You'll need a bigger **brush** to paint that wall.
Brush that dirt off your clothes before you come inside. *(1 mark)*

Q3 On **saturday**, I am going on holiday to **spain** with my parents. My friend **frances** and her family are coming too. *(1 mark)*

Q4 The **team** won the **competition**. The **fans** were filled with **joy** and **admiration**. *(1 mark)*

Verbs

Q1 Tim **walked** forty miles and **raised** some money for charity. *(1 mark)*

Q2 She **ride** her bike whenever she is bored. The correct spelling is **rides**. *(1 mark)*

Q3 **Emma** is the subject
ran is the verb
canal is the object *(1 mark)*

Q4 We **should** have a salad for lunch.
I **might** walk home this evening. *(1 mark)*

Adjectives

Q1 The hotel we stayed in was **fantastic**. It had **enormous** rooms and the beds were extremely **comfortable**. *(1 mark)*

Q2 E.g. new, red, woolly. *(1 mark)*

Q3 It was very **icy** on the roads today. Everyone at school was **miserable** because of the cold weather, but I was **hopeful** that it would get warmer soon. *(1 mark)*

Q4 I was very **annoyed** when I got lost in the city centre. I had to ask a **helpful** man for directions to the restaurant. *(1 mark)*

Adverbs

Q1 quickly *(1 mark)*

Q2 E.g. happily *(1 mark)*

Q3 tomorrow *(1 mark)*

Q4 I am **eagerly** looking forward to going shopping. I will **probably** buy myself a new pair of shoes. *(1 mark)*

Q5 **Despite the cold weather,** Annabelle wore her favourite flip-flops. *(1 mark)*

Prepositions

Q1 in *(1 mark)*

Q2 We played hide and seek **after** dinner. I hid **under** the stairs, Jill was **behind** the sofa, and Sarah shut herself **inside** the cupboard. *(1 mark)*

Q3 through *(1 mark)*

Pronouns

Q1 you me *(1 mark)*

Q2 She said that the skateboard in the shed is **yours** if you want it. *(1 mark)*

Q3 When we got to the beach, **it** was very busy.
My parents got stuck in traffic, so **they** were late for the show.
I walked over to John and asked **him** if he knew what time it was. *(1 mark)*

Determiners

Q1 I wanted **a** cup of hot chocolate, but we had no milk.
They didn't have any left at **the** local shop either.
While I was there, I bought some juice and **an** apple. *(1 mark)*

Q2 These *(1 mark)*

Q3 We ate **the** chicken and **five** potatoes for **our** dinner. *(1 mark)*

Q4 E.g. many, some, several, three, enough *(1 mark)*

Mixed Practice

Q1 noun *(1 mark)*

Q2 **Layla** is the subject
presents is the object *(1 mark)*

Q3 seriously — adverb
delicious — adjective
friendly — adjective
today — adverb *(1 mark)*

Q4 The house is **hers**.
The caravan is **theirs**.
The coat is **mine**. *(1 mark)*

Q5 My parents are definitely **interested** in buying one of the puppies. We went to visit them today, and they were very **playful**. *(1 mark)*

Answers

Q6 It was raining **yesterday**, so we **reluctantly** cancelled the match. *(1 mark)*

Q7 She said she **would** leave her house at lunchtime.
You **can** have a pudding when you finish your vegetables.
I know there **must** be a mop around here somewhere.
(1 mark)

Q8 After — B
her — A
the — C
enjoyable — D *(1 mark)*

Pages 37-46 — Sentences and Tenses

Sentences

Q1 a statement *(1 mark)*

Q2 *Example of a question beginning with 'what':* What time is it? *(1 mark)*

Q3 Buy the rabbit. *(1 mark)* *(This command could also end with an exclamation mark.)*

Q4 What a loud noise that was *(1 mark)*

Clauses and Phrases

Q1 When he saw us, **the otter swam away quickly**.
You must do your chores, even though you don't want to.
I returned the jumper because it was too big.
Since it was Friday, **Yasmin was allowed to stay up late**.
(1 mark)

Q2 main clause
subordinate clause
main clause *(1 mark)*

Q3 a subordinate clause *(1 mark)*

Q4 The happy little bird *(1 mark)*

Q5 **While I am on holiday**, I go to bed later than usual.
I ate the whole cake **although I soon felt sick**.
Tristram joined a tennis club **because he wanted to make new friends**.
Since she had been caught, the robber confessed to her crime. *(1 mark)*

Q6 *Example of a noun phrase:* the brown dog in the garden *(1 mark)*

Q7 After school, we're going to buy some sweets. *(1 mark)* *(The adverbial must be followed by a comma.)*

Conjunctions

Q1 Pari went to the school disco, **but** Omar felt too unwell to go.
Yesterday, Joe went to the park **and** to the shopping centre.
Juliette's dad cooked dinner **while** her mum was at the dentist. *(1 mark)*

Q2 We should stay inside **so** we don't get wet. It will be sunny again soon **and** we will continue our walk, **but** the ground may still be wet. *(1 mark)*

Q3 co-ordinating conjunction
subordinating conjunction
co-ordinating conjunction
(1 mark)

Active and Passive

Q1 He talked about helping others. *(1 mark)*

Q2 passive, active, passive *(1 mark)*

Q3 The plant was watered by Ellis. *(1 mark)*

Tenses

Q1 That coat in the window is not for sale. *(1 mark)*

Q2 Marco **asked** to play with us. He **joined** Lucy's team as the goalkeeper. Lucy and Marco **won** the game, but we'll win next time. *(1 mark)*

Q3 My hamster is called Butter. We got her two years ago. She **has lived** in a cage in my bedroom ever since.
(1 mark)

Formal and Informal Writing

Q1 children *(1 mark)*

Q2 I look forward to receiving your reply shortly.
My family usually remains at home for Christmas.
(1 mark)

Q3 formal, informal, informal *(1 mark)*

Q4 *Example of a possible answer:* Jane is not going to the party. *(1 mark)*

Standard and Non-Standard English

Q1 Yesterday, we **were** helping my aunt paint her kitchen. We **did** all of the work easily, so we haven't got **anything** to do now. *(1 mark)*

Q2 go, saw, any *(1 mark)*

Q3 Finish your lunch quickly so we can play outside.
(1 mark)

Mixed Practice

Q1 Although we won the game, **we thanked the other team**.
Lisa showed me her story while Jan was busy in the kitchen.
My mum made me stay at home because I felt unwell.
(1 mark)

Q2 Bring your work here — command
Which cake did you want — question
My house is on the next road — statement
How wonderful the show was — exclamation *(1 mark)*

Answers

Q3 **If** you're bored, try reading **or** drawing. You could also visit a friend **and** play a board game, **although** you might not win! *(1 mark)*

Q4 Samira has watched every rugby match this season. *(1 mark)*

Q5 did, strangely *(1 mark)*

Q6 E.g. think / believe *(1 mark)*

Q7 a noun phrase *(1 mark)*

Q8 Serena **moved** to Wales because her mum **got** a new job. *(1 mark)*

Q9 This house was built by my family. *(1 mark)*

Pages 47-57 — Punctuation

Punctuating Sentences

Q1 **next** weekend, **i** am going on a trip with my friend **susan**. **we** are catching the train to **edinburgh** on **saturday** morning. *(1 mark)*

Q2 Who do you think will win the cricket match *(1 mark)*

Q3 Gordon often goes walking in the mountains. He likes to take lots of photographs of the scenery. *(1 mark)*

Q4 "Look out**!**" Geraldine shouted as someone ran in front of her trolley. *(1 mark)*

Commas

Q1 The farmer's dogs include a collie, a labrador, a greyhound and a whippet. *(1 mark)*

Q2 At the corner shop I bought bread**,** a litre of milk and the local newspaper. *(1 mark)*

Q3 After feeding the seagulls**,** Bart got onto his bike and cycled home. *(1 mark)*

Q4 The first one suggests that only authors who study more write better books. The second suggests that all non-fiction authors study more than other authors. *(1 mark)*

Apostrophes

Q1 All of the artists' paintings were lost in the fire. *(1 mark)*

Q2 I'll need to run if I'm going to catch the start of the film. **Tiffany's** brother has seen it and he's said the beginning is the best part. *(1 mark)*

Q3 I have = I've
she will = she'll
should not = shouldn't
they are = they're *(1 mark)*

Q4 Sometimes, **Walters** cats go for a walk. **Theyll** often wander to Mrs **Williamss** house down the road. *(1 mark)*

Inverted Commas

Q1 "It is going to be cloudy today," said the weather reporter. *(1 mark)*

Q2 **"**What's all that noise?**"** Ayaka asked, after waking suddenly. *(1 mark)*

Q3 Replace the exclamation mark with a full stop. Put a comma after the word 'club'. *(1 mark)*

Colons, Semi-Colons and Dashes

Q1 Kath watched the sun rise — the sky was completely orange. *(1 mark)*

Q2 The bridge was shut for the day: there had been an accident. *(1 mark)*

Q3 The United Kingdom is made up of four nations**:** Scotland, England, Northern Ireland and Wales. *(1 mark)*

Q4 Umair looked at his phone**;** he found three new text messages. *(1 mark)*

Q5 Harold could tell it was Halloween — all the shops were selling pumpkins. *(1 mark)*

Q6 Damon ordered a bowl of pasta; a (large) slice of garlic bread; and a glass of apple juice. *(1 mark)*

Q7 colon *(1 mark)*

Adding Extra Information

Q1 Morgan — a qualified doctor — checked the man's pulse. *(1 mark)*

Q2 John asked Cindy**,** his brother's best friend**,** whether she was planning to run a marathon that year. *(1 mark)*

Q3 To add extra information. *(1 mark)*

Hyphens and Bullet Points

Q1 Imran finished the race in a record-breaking time. *(1 mark)*

Q2 At the gift shop, Owen buys:
- a T-shirt
- a cushion
- two postcards
- four coasters

(1 mark) (If the answer uses capitalisation, it should do so at the start of each point. The answer can also use either commas or semi-colons after the first three points, with a full stop after the fourth. The punctuation must be consistent to gain the mark.)

Q3 Samantha is friends with an actor and a well**-**dressed businessman. *(1 mark)*

Mixed Practice

Q1 **next** year, **i** am going on holiday to **spain** with my friend **sophie**. **we** have booked to travel in **april** when it is cooler. *(1 mark)*

Answers

Q2 The bus conductor replied, **"**Here's your change.**"** *(1 mark)*

Q3 brackets / commas *(1 mark)*

Q4 The museum had many amazing things on display**;** most of them had come from a similar exhibition in Germany. *(1 mark)*

Q5 I enjoy reading **childrens** books. They usually have exciting plots and interesting characters. *(1 mark)*

Q6 correctly, incorrectly, correctly, correctly *(1 mark)*

Q7 Phil's bad**-**tempered puppy tore up the carpet this morning. *(1 mark)*

Q8 A comma needs to be added:
"I think it's time for us to leave," Noel whispered to Cheryl. *(1 mark)*

Q9 dash / semi-colon / colon *(1 mark)*

Q10 Stanley has a list of jobs for today:
- wash the car
- take out the bins and the recycling
- clean the kitchen and the living room

(1 mark) (If the answer uses capitalisation, it should do so at the start of each point. The answer can also use either commas or semi-colons after the first three points, with a full stop after the fourth. The punctuation must be consistent to gain the mark.)

Q11a) After they met Mr Fisher, Claire and Rafael went to the restaurant.

Q11b) After they met**,** Mr Fisher**,** Claire and Rafael went to the restaurant. *(1 mark)*

Q12 colon *(1 mark)*

Pages 58-63 — Vocabulary

Prefixes

Q1 anti — clockwise
un — easy
auto — graph
de — activate
re — use
(1 mark)

Q2 **dis**belief, **mis**lead, **super**market, **re**visit *(1 mark)*

Q3 **re**turn, **mis**understood *(1 mark)*

Suffixes

Q1 treat — ment
walk — er
class — ify
personal — ise
soft — ness
(1 mark)

Q2 ly, ness *(1 mark)*

Q3 multiply, realise, simplify *(1 mark for all answers spelled correctly)*

Word Families

Q1 population *(1 mark)*

Q2 alone *(1 mark)*

Q3 stability, unstable *(1 mark)*

Q4 *1 mark for a sensible answer, e.g.* forecast, foresight, forewarn

Synonyms and Antonyms

Q1 regularly *(1 mark)*

Q2 ancient — modern
obstruct — assist
fascinating — uninteresting
appropriate — unsuitable
(1 mark)

Q3 precise, accurate *(1 mark)*

Q4 worse / inferior *(1 mark)*

Mixed Practice

Q1 superb, excellent *(1 mark)*

Q2 dis — appear
re — attach
mis — hear
(1 mark)

Q3 ly, ise *(1 mark)*

Q4 *1 mark for two suitable answers, e.g.* disgusting *and* close

Q5 *1 mark for 3 suitable answers, e.g.* **re**apply, **over**cook / **under**cook, **un**usual

Q6 run**ner**, pay**ment** *(1 mark for both answers spelled correctly)*

Q7 artistic, artist *(1 mark)*

Q8 clear *(1 mark)*

Pages 64-72 — Spelling

Plurals

Q1 puppies *(1 mark)*

Q2 es, s, es, *(1 mark)*

Q3 brushes, teeth, turkeys, shelves *(1 mark)*

Q4 My sister invited some **people** over for lunch today. We all had a salad with **tomatoes** and onion. I was still hungry afterwards, so I had a few **cherries**. *(1 mark)*

Prefixes and Suffixes

Q1 **disimilar** should be spelled **dissimilar** *(1 mark)*

Q2 begin**ning**, sit**ting**, laugh**ing**, garden**ing** *(1 mark)*

Q3 automobile, submarine, interact, superstar *(1 mark)*

Q4 special *(1 mark)*

Q5 meanness, dissolve, famous, limited *(1 mark)*

Q6 friendliness, simpler, continuous *(1 mark)*

Answers

Homophones

Q1 We went to the cinema because we were **bored**.
I asked my friends where they wanted to **meet** for lunch.
Ellie took a **piece** of paper and began to draw on it.
(1 mark)

Q2 an award — medal
above average — great
to interfere — meddle
to shred into pieces — grate
(1 mark)

Q3 seen, allowed, main, steal
(1 mark)

Silent Letters

Q1 gnarled *(1 mark)*

Q2 Jeremy **knew** the way to the bus station.
We felt very **doubtful** about the weather forecast that weekend.
I checked the time by looking at the watch on my **wrist**. *(1 mark)*

Q3 **carm** should be spelled **calm** *(1 mark)*

Q4 We saw the **design** for the new building as soon as we **walked** into her office.
We asked her about it, but she wouldn't **answer** our questions. *(1 mark)*

Spelling Tricky Words

Q1 ceiling *(1 mark)*

Q2 I had three **pieces** of pizza.
My best friend and I are in the same **science** class.
They decided that **neither** of the hotels was good enough.
(1 mark)

Q3 accept, supporter, message, success *(1 mark)*

Q4 **mashine** should be spelled **machine** *(1 mark)*

Q5 We always went into the house **through** the side door.
The cats often **fought** playfully with each other.
We **ought** to go and see how Curtis is feeling. *(1 mark)*

Q6 enough, impossible, access, school, apparent *(1 mark)*

Mixed Practice

Q1 knee *(1 mark)*

Q2 Dilma had **heard** the news on the radio.
I wasn't sure what to **wear** for the party.
The teacher started to **write** the instructions on the board. *(1 mark)*

Q3 The **thieves** tried to get into the house by climbing up the **branches**. The police managed to catch them because two **women** spotted them. *(1 mark)*

Q4 **nerveous** should be spelled **nervous** *(1 mark)*

Q5 I need to buy my friend's birthday present but I keep **forgetting**.
I didn't need to wash the car — it was **unnecessary** after so much rain.
On Saturdays we go **swimming** in the pool at the local leisure centre. *(1 mark)*

Q6 parachute, bought, unless, partial *(1 mark)*

Q7 Mandy **received** a postcard from Josh.
Claudia couldn't **believe** what she was hearing.
(1 mark)

Pages 73-77 — Practice Test 2

Q1 **one** *(1 mark)*

Q2 *1 mark for a sensible answer, e.g.* That they're close to the coast. *(1 mark)*

Q3 frightening *(1 mark)*

Q4 *1 mark for a sensible answer, e.g.* He thought its father would be even bigger so he was scared. *(1 mark)*

Q5 *1 mark for a sensible answer, e.g.* The two giants would have fought. *(1 mark)*

Q6 The Giant's Boot *and* The Camel *(1 mark)*

Q7 Things to see when you visit the Giant's Causeway
(1 mark)

Q8 surround *(1 mark)*

Q9 *1 mark for a simple answer, e.g.* The scientific explanation happened longer ago than the legend.
2 marks for giving a more detailed answer, e.g. The legend of Finn McCool took place 'thousands of years ago'. The scientific explanation describes events 'millions of years ago'.

Q10 Legends say that a giant built the Giant's Causeway.
(1 mark)

Q11 Amani paints a lot. She likes to draw too. *(1 mark)*

Q12 verb, adjective, adjective, verb *(1 mark)*

Q13 **m**y friend, **a**gnes, lives in **b**irmingham. **i** went to see her last **t**hursday.

Q14 **releif** should be spelled **relief** *(1 mark)*

Q15 *Example of a question beginning with 'which':*
Which shirt has a hole in it?
(1 mark)

Q16 **Ahmed's favourite subject is history,** although he likes geography too.
Even though it was nearby, **Amanda drove to the shop.**
(1 mark)

Q17 brackets *(1 mark)*

Q18 What a nice bird that is
(1 mark)

Q19 annoyed, irritated
(1 mark)